# Refuting Evolution 2

*Updated and Expanded*

## Jonathan Sarfati

CREATION
BOOK PUBLISHERS

# Refuting Evolution 2

by Jonathan Sarfati, Ph.D.

ISBN: 978-0-94990-627-4

Cover design by Luis Lovelace

Published by  **Creation Book Publishers**
P.O. Box 350
Powder Springs, GA 30127
Phone: 1-800-616-1264
creationbookpublishers.com

Please visit our website for further information on the Christian worldview and the creation/evolution issue:

**CREATION.com**

# Acknowledgements

Mike Matthews: for editing the material from my original web rebuttals and ordering it logically into the chapters for this book in the original 2002 edition, so it could be a stand-alone book.

Lita Cosner: for helping to update the information for the second edition, since there have been many advances in science since the first edition.

My dear wife, Sherry: for her love and support.

# Contents

# UNIT 3 Claim: "Problems" with Evolution are Illusionary

# Introduction

Belief in creation is 'nonsense.' Creation is "a religious view that has nothing to do with science." Daily, the airwaves and newspaper racks are filled with such inflammatory claims.

The barrage of new arguments and scientific 'evidence' that 'prove' evolution can seem overwhelming to believers in the Word of God, who are ridiculed as irrational religious zealots who still live in the dark ages because they believe the Bible's fables about creation. It is more crucial than ever that believers are 'ready' to defend their faith (1 Peter 3:15).

This book pulls together the most powerful arguments that Christians are likely to hear from today's leading evolutionary scientists. These arguments come from two powerhouses in the media—PBS-TV and the journal *Scientific American*—which have taken up the mantle of the pro-evolution crusade, preaching their message to a broad market around the world. PBS summarized the modern arguments for evolution in its lavish eight-hour series on *Evolution*, which still re-airs and is shown in schools across America. It has also aired in Australia. *Scientific American* pulled together its own best arguments in a combative cover story, "15 Answers to Creationist Nonsense."

## PBS-TV's Evolution series—multimillion-dollar propaganda

The Public Broadcasting Service (PBS) first aired its ambitious TV series *Evolution* in September 2001. Co-produced by Clear Blue Sky Productions (founded and chaired by Microsoft billionaire Paul Allen), *Evolution* had almost unlimited funding. In addition to the TV series, the producers launched an aggressive campaign to fully equip teachers to indoctrinate young people in molecules-to-man evolution. This propaganda effort included "an unprecedented array of resources for further learning at home and in school" (their own words), including a free teacher's guide, an interactive Web site, a multimedia Web library, teacher videos, monthly newsletters, student lessons and teacher training workshops.

To avoid the impression that *Evolution* was one-sided propaganda, the producers claimed that they invited the Discovery Institute, part of the 'intelligent design' movement,[1] for 'balance'. But the Discovery Institute declined because they would have been slotted in the 'religious' objections segments, whereas their objections to evolution are purely scientific. By failing to provide space to the scientific criticism of evolution, the PBS/Nova series gave the impression that the only criticisms of evolution are 'religious'. They also ignored the self-declared atheistic faith of many of evolution's proponents, including several of those involved in the series, e.g. Richard Dawkins, Daniel Dennett, the late Stephen Jay Gould, Edward O. Wilson and Eugenie Scott.

The PBS overview of this program leaves no doubts about the producers' worshipful attitude toward evolution:

> Evolution plays a critical role in our daily lives, yet it is one of the most overlooked principles of life. It is the mechanism that determines who lives, who dies, and who gets the opportunity to pass traits on to the next generation, and the next, and the next. ... Evolution [is] the underpinning of all of biology, affecting our health, our food supply and the vast web of life. ... It's such a simple theory, yet we see millions of examples of it at work in our everyday lives....
>
> The goal of *Evolution* is to heighten public awareness about what evolution is and how it works, and to dispel common misunderstandings. The project seeks to illuminate why evolution is relevant, to improve its teaching, and to encourage a national dialogue on the issues currently surrounding this science.[2]

1.    See Wieland, C., "CMI's views on the Intelligent Design Movement," creation.com/idm, 30 August 2002.

2.    PBS Web site, "Evolution project overview," www.pbs.org/wgbh/evolution/about/overview_project.html.

Such in-your-face propaganda demands an answer from Christians who believe the biblical account of origins.

## Scientific American's '15 Answers to Creationist Nonsense'

Scientific American is a semi-popular journal which publishes attractively illustrated and fairly detailed, but not overly technical, articles, mostly on science. It is not a peer-reviewed journal like Nature or the in-depth Journal of Creation,[3] but many of its articles are very useful.

Yet behind the surface is a deeper agenda. The most recent editors, as will be explained in this book, have been working to push an atheistic worldview. Further, they have been pushing a number of corollaries in the guise of 'science', such as a radical pro-abortion, human cloning and population control agenda.

Evidence of Scientific American's agenda was its refusal to hire a science writer named Forrest Mims III after he admitted he was a creationist and pro-life. The editor who rejected Mims admitted that his work was 'fabulous', 'great' and 'first rate', and 'should be published somewhere'.[4] Scientific American subsequently published an article about his revolutionary atmospheric haze detector, although it did not mention the incident of blatant discrimination.[5]

John Rennie (b. 1959), editor in chief from 1994 to 2009, has fervently promoted the anti-God evolution agenda. Like many anti-creationist propagandists, he often launches into attacks against creationists with a poor understanding of their position. Additionally, he has only a bachelor's degree in science, so is far less qualified than the leading creationist scientists, who have

---

3. Published by Creation Ministries International.

4. "Science's Litmus Test" (telephone transcript of conversation between Forrest Mims and Jonathan Piel, then editor of Scientific American), Harper's Magazine, March 1991. The transcript makes it clear that an outstanding writer was not hired for disbelieving in the sacred cow of evolution (and a 'woman's right to choose' [to kill her unborn]).

5. Carlson, S., "The amateur scientist," Scientific American 276(5):80–81, May 1997.

Ph.D.s from leading secular universities.[6]

Yet this did not stop his activism at the height of the controversy in Kansas over changes to de-emphasize evolution in the state education standards. Rennie personally urged scientists on university admissions committees to adopt 'big stick' tactics in bullying the Kansas governor and the state board of education. He urged them to proclaim that 'in light of the newly lowered education standards in Kansas, the qualifications of any students applying from that state in the future will have to be considered very carefully.'[7] In logic, this is known as the fallacy of *Argumentum ad baculum*, i.e. 'Agree with me or else unpleasant consequences will follow!' Rennie is far from the only evolutionist to resort to this.

Rennie became more actively involved in the fray, taking on the role of the valiant B.Sc. scientist trying to stem the creationist tide. His diatribe "15 Answers to Creationist Nonsense" is subtitled "Opponents of evolution want to make a place for creationism by tearing down real science, but their arguments don't hold up." Even the magazine's cover had splashed on the top, "15 ways to expose creationist nonsense."

But as will be shown, Rennie—and the anti-creationist leaders that he represents—have only the vaguest ideas about real creationist arguments. Many of the 'creationist arguments' that they attack are straw men which serious creationists have also rejected. (These bad arguments are listed in Appendix 2 of this book, page 219.) Rennie's other arguments in defense of evolution are also nothing new, and have been mostly answered on the *Creation Ministries International* website creation.com. One purpose of this book is to help Christians recognize and answer the logical fallacies common among evolutionists, including inconsistent definitions of the word 'evolution'—*equivocation*, and failure to differentiate between 'origins science' and 'operational science' (explained in detail on page 22). It will also point out that evolutionary belief is largely a deduction from materialistic axioms, which Rennie actually acknowledges, and lamely tries to defend.

---

6      See for example creation.com/creation-scientists.

7.     Cited in: Johnson, P., *The Wedge of Truth: Splitting the Foundations of Naturalism*, p. 80, InterVarsity Press, Illinois, 2000.

Rennie argues that creation has no place in science and has done nothing for the advancement of science. Yet he completely misses the irony that *Scientific American* was founded by a staunch believer in creation—the artist and inventor Rufus Porter (1792–1884), who thought that science glorified the creator God. In the very first issue, his editorial stated:

> We shall advocate the pure Christian religion, without favouring any particular sect ... .[8]

The founder of *Scientific American* also wrote an astonishing article in that issue, 'Rational Religion', which bluntly declares that we all depend on the Creator God, who revealed Himself in Holy Scripture. Porter's godly admonition is worth rereading:

> First, then, let us, as rational creatures, be ever ready to acknowledge God as our Creator and daily Preserver; and that we are each of us individually dependant on his special care and good will towards us, in supporting the wonderful action of nature which constitutes our existence; and in preserving us from the casualties, to which our complicated and delicate structure is liable. Let us also, knowing our entire dependence on Divine Benevolence, as rational creatures, do ourselves the honor to express personally and frequently, our thanks to him for his goodness; and to present our petitions to Him for the favours which we constantly require. This course is rational, even without the aid of revelation: but being specially invited to this course, by the divine word, and assured of the readiness of our Creator to answer our prayers and recognize our thanks, it is truly surprising that any rational being, who has ever read the inspired writings should willingly forego this privilege, or should be ashamed to be seen engaged in this rational employment, or to have it known that he practices it.[9]

Christianity *is rational.* The purpose behind this book is to encourage believers in the absolute authority of God's revealed

---

8.    Porter, R., To the American public, *Scientific American* **1**(1), 1845.
9.    Porter, R., Rational religion, *Scientific American* **1**(1), 1845.

Word. Further, it's to give them ammunition to *disseminate* this truth. This includes defending the foundational truths found in Genesis (1 Peter 3:15, Jude 3), and refute the arguments of unbelieving scientists (2 Corinthians 10:4–5).

My previous book, *Refuting Evolution* (1999, updated 2007), gave teachers, students and parents answers to the influential publication *Teaching About Evolution and the Nature of Science* (1998), a standard reference for science teachers produced by the US National Academy of Sciences. This new book was inspired by two more recent statements of evolutionary beliefs: the PBS-TV series *Evolution* and a *Scientific American* broadside titled '15 Answers to Creationist Nonsense.' If Christians can digest these arguments, along with the straightforward rebuttals, they will be fully equipped to answer even the best arguments thrown at them by their peers, teachers, neighbors and nonbelievers with whom they share the Gospel.

The material for this book was taken from my series on the PBS/Nova series creation.com/pbs, and my response to *Scientific American*'s article creation.com/sciam. The appendices are taken from the *Creation Answers Book*, which I co-authored (under the editorship of Dr Don Batten), and CMI's most popular web article "Arguments we think creationists should not use", which was mainly my anonymous authorship. None other than Richard Dawkins commended the existence of such an article.

*Note about citations:* Quotations from the *Scientific American* article by John Rennie will be labeled SA, followed by the page number. Quotations from and other mentions of the PBS-TV *Evolution* series will be labeled PBS, followed by the episode number, e.g. PBS 6 refers to Episode 6. The seven PBS episodes have these titles:

Episode 1:   Darwin's dangerous idea
Episode 2:   Great transformations
Episode 3:   Extinction!
Episode 4:   The evolutionary arms race!
Episode 5:   Why sex?

Episode 6:   The mind's big bang
Episode 7:   What about God?

*Creation*, formerly *Creation Ex Nihilo* (before that *Ex Nihilo*), is the *Creation Ministries International* international quarterly magazine.  *Journal of Creation* (*JoC*), formerly *TJ* (before that *Creation Ex Nihilo Technical Journal*), is the *Creation Ministries International* international peer-reviewed journal for advanced topics in creation.  In this book, it will always be cited as *JoC* even before this new name was adopted.

# UNIT 1

## CLAIM:

# Evolution is Science

*Evolutionists insist that evolutionary theory is science, but creationism is religion.*

# Chapter 1

# Argument:
# Creationism is Religion, Not Science

*Evolutionists say, 'Creationism is a
belief system that has nothing to do
with science.'*

The two-hour premier episode of the PBS/Nova series *Evolution* sets the tone for this propaganda effort—ridiculing biblical religion as the enemy of true science, which had long shackled scientific study. Much of the first episode is a dramatization of the life of Charles Darwin (1809–1882). It opens with Darwin's famous voyage on HMS *Beagle*. Darwin introduces himself and Captain Robert FitzRoy (1805–1865) in broken Spanish to villagers in South America. The villagers then lead Darwin and FitzRoy to the skull of an extinct ground sloth, and this conversation ensues:

> **Darwin: I wonder why these creatures no longer exist.**
>
> **FitzRoy: Perhaps the Ark was too small to allow them entry and they perished in the Flood.**
>
> **D: [laughs]**
>
> **F: What is there to laugh at?**
>
> **D: Nothing, nothing.**
>
> **F: Do you mock me or the Bible?**
>
> **D: Neither.**

F: What sort of clergyman will you be, Mr Darwin?

D: Dreadful, dreadful.

Then the drama moves to a scene on the *Beagle*, where Captain FitzRoy is reading from Genesis 1, and Darwin is below deck rolling his eyes.

There we have it—the alleged struggle between science and 'fundamentalist' religion. Of course, the representative of 'fundamentalism', Captain FitzRoy, is made to spout a silly straw man argument. Nowhere is there any hint that there could be any scientific objections to evolution.

But FitzRoy's argument is unbiblical—the Bible clearly states that two of *every* kind of land vertebrate animal was on the Ark, and the Ark had plenty of room for all the required animals.[1,2]

But then—not that we should be surprised—the PBS dramatization goes well beyond artistic license and actually falsifies history. Darwin's anti-Christianity hadn't fully developed by the time of the *Beagle* voyage, and he even attended church services, while FitzRoy likely didn't believe in a global Flood during that voyage. After all, FitzRoy himself had given Darwin a welcoming gift of the long-age–advocating book *Principles of Geology* by Charles Lyell (1797–1875), which was a great inspiration for Darwin's evolutionary ideas, as will be shown later in this book.

---

1.　Sarfati, J., "How did all the animals fit on Noah's Ark?" *Creation* **19**(2):16–19, 1997, creation.com/arkanimals; Woodmorappe, J., *Noah's Ark: A Feasibility Study*, Institute for Creation Research, El Cajon, CA, 1996.

2.　This includes dinosaurs. Skeptics overlook a number of things, and recent scientific research since the first edition of this book makes the creationist case even easier: the Ark was huge; many dinosaurs were small; even the big ones started life off in eggs no larger than footballs; growth rings on their bones show that they went through a growth spurt so they could have been on the Ark before this; dinosaur names have been multiplied so that they were represented by comparatively few 'kinds', baby or 'teen' dinosaurs have sometimes been given different names to the adult specimens. Recent summaries of the new evidence are "Shrinking dino numbers," *Creation* **33**(1):8, 2011 and "Dino puberty blues," creation.com/dino-puberty-blues.

## Philosophical assumption behind 'modern science'—naturalism

The media is not subtle about its ridicule of 'creation science.' John Rennie gets right to the point in '15 Answers to Creationist Nonsense.' He asserts:

> 'Creation science' is a contradiction in terms. A central tenet of modern science is methodological naturalism—it seeks to explain the universe purely in terms of observed or testable natural mechanisms. [*SA* 84]

Now we get to the key issue. It's not about scientific facts at all, but self-serving materialistic 'rules of the game' by which the evolutionary establishment interprets the facts.[3] So it should be instructive for people to understand what's really driving Rennie and his ilk—a materialist or naturalist agenda that excludes God. This is not a tenet deducible by the experimental method, but a philosophical assumption from *outside* science.

Rennie illustrates his view of 'modern science' with an example from physics:

> Physics describes the atomic nucleus with specific concepts governing matter and energy, and it tests those descriptions experimentally. Physicists introduce new particles, such as quarks, to flesh out their theories only when data show that the previous descriptions cannot adequately explain observed phenomena. The new particles do not have arbitrary properties, moreover— their definitions are tightly constrained, because the new particles must fit within the existing framework of physics. [*SA* 84–85]

What has this to do with evolution? Creationists agree that the particles would not behave arbitrarily, because they were created by a God of order. But an atheist has no philosophical justification from his underlying religious premise, i.e. 'God does

---

3.  See Wieland, C., "The rules of the game," *Creation* 11(1):47–50, 1988, creation.com/rules.

not exist', for a belief in an orderly universe.[4]

## Deceptive attacks on creation 'science'

Evolutionists tend to lump all opponents of materialistic 'science' under the same category, whether they call it 'creation science' or 'intelligent design', ignoring the profound differences among the various camps. As a result, they make some outlandish claims that simply do not apply to Bible-believing Christians. For instance, *Scientific American* attacks 'creation science' because it promotes some shadowy intelligence that is beyond scientific inquiry and that offers few answers to scientific questions:

> Intelligent-design theorists invoke shadowy entities that conveniently have whatever unconstrained abilities are needed to solve the mystery at hand. Rather than expanding scientific inquiry, such answers shut it down. (How does one disprove the existence of omnipotent intelligences?)

> Intelligent design offers few answers. For instance, when and how did a designing intelligence intervene in life's history? By creating the first DNA? The first cell? The first human? Was every species designed, or just a few early ones? Proponents of intelligent-design theory frequently decline to be pinned down on these points. They do not even make real attempts to reconcile their disparate ideas about intelligent design. [*SA* 85]

In reality, the founders and leaders of modern 'creation science' base their views on the Bible, believing it is God's inspired account of history given to mankind. It is wrong to confuse this group with other, more recent advocates of 'intelligent design' who wish to avoid all appeals to biblical authority. Christians don't advocate just any 'designer' who may or may not be capricious. Rather, they identify the Designer with the faithful Triune God of the Bible.[5]

---

4. See also Sarfati, J., "Why does science work at all?" *Creation* **31**(3):12–14, 2009; and "The biblical roots of modern science," *Creation* **32**(4), 2010; creation.com/roots.

5. See Sarfati, J., *By Design*, Creation Book Publishers, Atlanta, 2008.

We base our science on the biblical framework of history, which provides much information about when and how the Designer performed special acts of design. That is, during Creation Week about 6,000 years ago, He created distinct kinds of creatures. Shortly after that, Adam sinned and brought death and mutations into the world. About 1,500 years later, God judged the world by a global Flood that produced most of the world's fossils. But two of every kind of land vertebrate (seven pairs of the few 'clean' ones and birds) were rescued on an ocean-liner–sized Ark. After they landed on the mountains of Ararat, the Ark animals migrated and diversified, adapting to different environments—including some speciation. Mankind disobeyed God's command to fill the Earth, and migrated only when God confused the languages at Babel about 100 years later. This explains why human fossils are higher in the post-Flood fossil record than other mammals.

Evolutionists often attack advocates of intelligent design for perfectly admissible types of logical arguments (which evolutionists also use). For instance, *Scientific American* condemns advocates of intelligent design because:

> [T]hey pursue argument by exclusion—that is, they belittle evolutionary explanations as far-fetched or incomplete and then imply that only design-based alternatives remain. [*SA* 85]

This is a valid argument though. It is simple logic, called the Law of the Excluded Middle.[6] Evolutionists from Darwin to today have used the same tactic, i.e. 'God wouldn't have done it that way, therefore evolution must explain it.'

It's notable that Darwin often used such pseudo-theological arguments *against* design rather than direct arguments *for* evolution. But this form of argument presupposes the 'two-model approach', i.e. that creation and evolution are the only alternatives, so evidence against creation is evidence for evolution.[7] Ironically, many evolutionists scream loudly if creationists use this same

6.   Sarfati, J.D., "Loving God with all your mind: Logic and Creation," *JoC* 12(2):142–151, 1998, creation.com/logic.

7.   See Doyle, S., "Vestigial arguments: remnants of evolution," 11 June 2008, creation.com/vestigialarguments.

form of logic to conclude that evidence against evolution is support for creation!

*Scientific American* goes on to claim,

> Logically, this is misleading: even if one naturalistic explanation is flawed, it does not mean that all are. [*SA* 85]

This attack overlooks the obvious fact that the 'intelligent design' arguments are based on *analogy*, a common scientific procedure, about what we can observe being produced by intelligent and unintelligent causes. There is nothing wrong or 'misleading' about that approach. The article continues with another misleading objection:

> Moreover, it does not make one intelligent-design theory more reasonable than another. Listeners are essentially left to fill in the blanks for themselves, and some will undoubtedly do so by substituting their religious beliefs for scientific ideas. [*SA* 85]

Here *Scientific American* is accusing their opponents of doing something that evolutionists do all the time. John Rennie has no objection to substituting (and confusing) his own atheistic religious ideas for scientific ones, but he finds it offensive when other people's religious ideas are brought into the discussion!

## Confusing 'origins science' with 'operational science'; the real origins of science

*Scientific American* also repeats the common claim that evolution and 'methodological naturalism' are the basis for modern advances in science:

> Time and again, science has shown that methodological naturalism can push back ignorance, finding increasingly detailed and informative answers to mysteries that once seemed impenetrable: the nature of light, the causes of disease, how the brain works. Evolution is doing the same with the riddle of how the living world took shape. [*SA* 85]

This fails to note the distinction between *normal (operational) science*, and *origins* or *historical science*.[8] Normal (operational) science deals only with repeatable observable processes in the *present*, while origins science helps us to make educated guesses about origins in the *past*, and deals with one-time unrepeatable events.

**Operational science** has indeed been very successful in understanding the world, and has led to many improvements in the quality of life, e.g. building technology and curing diseases, as well as putting men on the moon. And it's vital to note that many historians, of a wide number of religious persuasions from Christians to atheists, point out that the founders of operational science were motivated by their belief that the universe was made by a rational Creator. An orderly universe makes perfect sense only if it were made by an orderly Creator. But there is no way to deduce an orderly universe from an atheistic or polytheistic system.[9]

Genesis 1:28 gives us permission to investigate creation, unlike say animism or pantheism that teaches that the creation itself is divine. And since God is sovereign, He was free to create as He pleased. So where the Bible is silent, the only way to find out how His creation works is to *experiment*, instead of relying on man-made philosophies as did the ancient Greeks.

These founding scientists, like modern creationists, regarded 'natural laws' as *descriptions* of the way God upholds His creation in a *regular* and *repeatable* way (Colossians 1:15–17), while miracles are God's way of upholding his creation in a special way for special reasons. Because creation *finished* at the end of Day 6 (Genesis 2:1), creationists following the Bible would expect that God has since mostly worked through 'natural laws' except where He has revealed in the Bible that He used a miracle. And since 'natural laws' are descriptive, not prescriptive, they cannot rule out miracles. Scientific laws do not cause or forbid anything any

8.    Sarfati, J, *Refuting Evolution*, 2 ed. ch. 1, Creation Book Publishers, Atlanta, 2008.

9.    Sarfati, J, "The Biblical Roots of Modern Science," *Creation* **32**(4): 32–36, 2010; creation.com/roots.

more than the outline of a map causes the shape of the coastline.[10]

Because God *finished* creating at the end of Day 6, biblical creationists would try to find natural laws for every aspect of operation science, and would not invoke a miracle to explain any repeating event in nature *in the present,* despite Scientific American's scare tactics. This can be shown in a letter I wrote to an enquirer who believed that atoms had to be held together by miraculous means:

> 'Natural laws' also help us make predictions about future events. In the case of the atom, the explanation of the electrons staying in their orbitals is the positive electric charge and large mass of the nucleus. This enables us to make predictions about how strongly a particular electron is held by a particular atom, for example, making the science of chemistry possible. While this is certainly an example of Col. 1:17, simply saying 'God upholds the electron' doesn't help us make predictions.

And in my days as a university teaching assistant before joining CMI, I marked an examination answer *wrong* because it said 'God made it so' for a question about the frequency of infrared spectral lines, instead of discussing atomic masses and force constants. So *Scientific American* is wrong to imply that creationists are in any way hindered in real operational science research, either in theory or in practice.

In contrast, evolution is a speculation about the unobservable and unrepeatable *past.* Thus it comes under *origins science.* Rather than observation, origins science uses the principles of *causality* (everything that has a beginning has a cause[11,12,13]) and

---

10. See also discussions in my web responses creation.com/miracles (2006) and creation.com/science-laws-speciation (2010).

11. Sarfati, J., "If God created the universe, then who created God?" *JoC* **12**(1)20–22, 1998, creation.com/whomadegod.

12. Sarfati, J., "The old 'Who created God?' canard revisited: Who designed the Designer?" creation.com/whodesigned, 17 November 2007.

13. Batten, D., "Who created God? It's an illogical question," *Creation* **32**(4):18–20, 2010; creation.com/who-created-god.

*analogy* (e.g. we observe that intelligence is needed to generate complex coded information in the present, so we can reasonably assume the same for the past). And because there was no material intelligent designer for life, it is legitimate to invoke a non-material designer for life. Creationists invoke the miraculous only for origins science, and for certain points in biblical history where the Bible teaches the miraculous, such as Creation, Fall and Flood. But as shown, this does *not* mean they will invoke it for operational science.[18]

Understanding the difference between operational and origins science is important so that one can see through common silly assertions such as:

> ... evolution is as thoroughly established as the picture of the solar system due to Copernicus, Galileo, Kepler, and Newton.

However, we can *observe* the motion of the planets, but no one has ever observed an information-increasing change of one type of organism to another.

To explain further: the laws that govern the *operation* of a computer are not those that made the computer in the first place. Much anti-creationist propaganda is like saying that if we concede that a computer had an intelligent designer, then we might not analyse a computer's workings in terms of natural laws of electron motion through semiconductors, and might think there are little intelligent beings pushing electrons around instead. Similarly, believing that the genetic code was originally designed does not preclude us from believing that it works entirely by the laws of chemistry involving DNA, RNA, proteins, etc. Conversely, the fact that the coding machinery works according to reproducible laws of chemistry does not prove that the laws of chemistry were sufficient to build such a system from a primordial soup. The PBS producer even admitted that the naturalistic origin of life was as a major problem for evolution (see page 54–55 ff.).

For some specifics, it's notable that *creationists* have made many of the great scientific advances that *Scientific American* and other evolutionary magazines like to mention! Isaac Newton discovered the spectrum of light (as well as co-inventing calculus and formulating the laws of motion and gravity); James Clerk Maxwell discovered the laws of electromagnetism which led to the prediction of electromagnetic radiation; Louis Pasteur formulated the germ theory of disease and disproved spontaneous generation; Joseph Lister pioneered antiseptic surgery; Raymond Damadian pioneered magnetic resonance imaging (MRI) that is a vital tool in brain research.[14]

In spite of the evidence, *Scientific American* asserts,

Creationism, by any name, adds nothing of intellectual value to the effort. [*SA* 85]

This blind assertion shows John Rennie's willing ignorance concerning the contributions made by creationists to the major branches of modern science in general and to his own magazine in particular.

## Example of the naturalistic assumptions driving evolution

Scientists have a reputation for impartiality and rigid honesty in their treatment of the facts, but it does not take much digging to find examples of how powerfully a materialistic mindset can cloud a scientist's judgment. One of the greatest influences on Darwin, for example, was a book he took on the *Beagle* voyage, *Principles of Geology* by Charles Lyell, which pushed the idea of slow and gradual geological processes occurring over millions of years, and denied Noah's Flood. Modern evolutionists acknowledge that Lyell was biased and unscientific, driven by anti-biblical philosophical assumptions, whereas the 'catastrophists' of his day (who believed in a Flood catastrophe) were rigid followers of the scientific method. Stephen J. Gould (1941–2002), himself a leading evolutionist, wrote:

Charles Lyell was a lawyer by profession, and his

---

14. See Wieland, C., "The not-so-Nobel decision," *Creation* 26(4):40–42, 2004, creation.com/mri; Sarfati, J., "Dr Damadian's vital contribution to MRI Nobel prize controversy returns," creation.com/damadian, 21–22 October 2006.

book is one of the most brilliant briefs published by an advocate. ... Lyell relied upon two bits of cunning to establish his uniformitarian views as the only true geology. First, he set up a straw man to demolish. ... In fact, the catastrophists were much more empirically minded than Lyell. The geologic record does seem to require catastrophes: rocks are fractured and contorted; whole faunas are wiped out. To circumvent this literal appearance, Lyell imposed his imagination upon the evidence. The geologic record, he argued, is extremely imperfect and we must interpolate into it what we can reasonably infer but cannot see. The catastrophists were the hard-nosed empiricists of their day, not the blinded theological apologists.[15]

One infamous example of Lyell's bias was his decision to ignore eyewitness accounts of the rate of erosion of the Niagara Falls, and publish a different figure to suit his purpose.[16]

But Lyell convinced Darwin, who eventually linked slow and gradual geological processes with slow and gradual biological processes. For example, he said that mountains were products of thousands of small rises. PBS Episode 1 portrays Darwin saying, 'Time, unimaginable tracts of time, is the key,' and arguing that just as small changes over ages can throw up mountains, why couldn't small changes accumulate over ages in animals to produce new structures?

## Scopes Trial and *Sputnik*

Evolutionists frequently point to two emotion-charged incidents in the twentieth century that supposedly confirm the danger of mixing creation and science—the famous Scopes Trial (1925) and the launch of *Sputnik* (1959). PBS 7 talks about the Scopes Trial and says that William Jennings Bryan was victorious, and that it had the 'chilling effect' of expunging evolution from science curricula from many states. Surprisingly, for a series

15. Gould, S., *Natural History* p. 16, February 1975.

16. Pierce, L., "Niagara Falls and the Bible," *Creation* **22**(4):8–13, 2000, creation.com/niagra.

containing millions of dollars worth of misinformation, it didn't present *Inherit the Wind* as a serious account of the trial. A good thing, because of its gross distortions documented in the article "*Inherit the Wind*—an historical analysis."[17]

Then PBS 7 showed *Sputnik*, and claimed that American authorities were so alarmed that the Soviets beat them into space that they decided to make science education a priority. Somehow evolution was smuggled in there. However, the science that put spacecraft on the moon is nothing like evolution. Rocket science involves repeatable experiments in the observable *present*; evolution is a just-so story to explain the unobservable *past* without God's direct intervention. It's especially ironic that the leader of the Apollo program, Wernher von Braun, was a creationist!

It's also blatantly revisionist history to claim that the Scopes Trial paved the way for *Sputnik*. During this alleged scientific nadir between Scopes and *Sputnik*, American schools produced more Nobel prizes than the rest of the world combined. This was especially pronounced in the biological field (physiology and medicine), supposedly one that can't do without evolution— America produced *twice* as many as all other countries. The Soviet Union beat the USA into space merely because the totalitarian government made it a top priority. While the USA had a good space program, there were other spending priorities, such as helping a war-torn world to rebuild. When the USA put its mind to it, it quickly surpassed the USSR, and was the first to land men on the moon in 1969. If it had needed scientists trained in evolution, the moon landing wouldn't have happened till the next generation had gone through the public school system.[18]

PBS and science journals are not the only ones trying to equate 'science' with evolution. One of the most vociferous anti-creationist organizations is the pretentiously named National

---

17. Demick, D., "Who's inheriting the wind now?" *Creation* **29**(2):34–36, 2007, creation.com/scopeswind.

18. The Discovery Institute's critique makes these good points in *Getting the Facts Straight: A Viewer's Guide to PBS's Evolution*, Discovery Institute Press, Seattle, 2001.

Center for Science Education. This is a humanist-founded organization, and its chief spokesperson, Eugenie Scott, is the winner of humanist awards and was also a consultant for the PBS series. It's significant that the only 'science education' NCSE seems interested in is evolution—not chemistry, physics, astronomy, or even experimental biology (or rocket science for that matter).[19]

## Creation in public schools?

The debate about religion and science has practical ramifications today, and it has spilled over into the public schools again. Evolutionists are terrified that criticisms of evolution (which they equate with teaching biblical creation—when it suits them!) may be allowed into the schools, and they are doing everything they can to stop it. (It's important to note that, although it would be nice to give teachers the *freedom* to present alternatives to evolution, CMI and other major creationist organizations have *not* been lobbying for compulsory creation in schools, despite common accusations. For one thing, one school of thought is that sending kids to public schools is like Moses sending the Israelite children to Canaanite schools. But mainly, would Christians want an atheistic teacher to be forced to teach creation, and deliberately distort it?)

The PBS program *Evolution* extensively featured Jefferson High School (in Lafayette, Indiana, USA). A student petition requested that the science curriculum should include the creation model. One teacher admitted that the signatories included 'outstanding students' and even some teachers. Of course this shows that one can be a top student without swallowing the evolutionary story.

But several teachers claimed the petition was dangerous (i.e. for them to listen to students and parents). One teacher, Clare McKinney, claimed to be a Christian, but she claimed that science can't involve God, swallowing the belief that science and religion do not overlap.

Yet this claim is only possible if the Bible and the real world

19. See "How religiously neutral are the anti-creationist organizations?" creation.com/neutral; "A who's who of evolutionists," *Creation* **20**(1):32, 1997, creation.com/who.

have nothing to do with each other, or if God and reason are mutually exclusive. Furthermore, even if the *evidence* is drawn from the natural world, it doesn't follow that the *explanations* for the evidence are confined to this world. Indeed, Newton's law of gravity was criticized for postulating an 'occult' action-at-a-distance force, and his predecessor Galileo likewise published his observations about motions while refusing to speculate about underlying causes. The philosopher Larry Laudan, a staunch anti-creationist, nevertheless criticized Judge Overton's ruling in the 1981/2 Arkansas 'McLean' creation science trial in his critique Science at the Bar—Causes for Concern:[20]

> For centuries scientists have recognized a difference between establishing the existence of a phenomenon and explaining that phenomenon in a law-like way. Our ultimate goal, no doubt, is to do both. But to suggest, as the McLean Opinion does repeatedly, that an existence claim (e.g., there was a worldwide flood) is unscientific until we have found the laws on which the alleged phenomenon depends is simply outrageous.
>
> Galileo and Newton took themselves to have established the existence of gravitational phenomena, long before anyone was able to give a causal or explanatory account of gravitation. Darwin took himself to have established the existence of natural selection almost a half-century before geneticists were able to lay out the laws of heredity on which natural selection depended.
>
> If we took the McLean Opinion criterion seriously, we should have to say that Newton and Darwin were unscientific; and, to take an example from our own time, it would follow that plate tectonics is unscientific because we have not yet identified the laws of physics and chemistry which account for the dynamics of crustal motion.

---

20. Laudan, L., "Science at the Bar—Causes for Concern," in Ruse, M., editor, *But Is it Science?* pp. 351–355, Prometheus Books, Buffalo, NY, 1988.

Another teacher at the school said that science is peer-reviewed, testable and repeatable. He failed to explain how a claim such as 'a reptile turned into a bird 150 million years ago' is testable or repeatable! Although evolutionists like to condemn creation as non-science, they have a hard time coming up with a definition of 'science' that includes evolution and excludes creation unless it's blatantly self-serving. Even some anti-creationist philosophers of science have strongly criticised the evolutionary scientific and legal establishment over these word games. They rightly point out that we should be more interested in whether creation is *true* or *false* than whether it meets some self-serving criteria for 'science'.[21]  Sometimes these definitions are self-contradictory, e.g. some have claimed, 'Creation is not scientific because it's not *testable*', then explained how it has allegedly been *tested* and shown to be wrong.

The school board, led by the school superintendent Ed Eiler, refused the Jefferson High School petition, claiming that creation is not part of science. Amazingly, the teacher Clare McKinney lamented how biology would be unteachable if evolution were censored, but that was *not* what the petitioners requested. Ironically, they wanted the curriculum to teach *more* about evolution than the establishment wants the students to learn! But the upshot was that any criticisms of evolution are censored instead.

There are numerous instances of teachers who face severe discrimination simply because they want to present their classes with the *scientific* evidence against evolution.[22]

When tested by logic and reality, the evolutionists' contention that 'creationism is a religion that has nothing to do with science' is hypocritical. Evolutionist Michael Ruse later admitted:

21.  Laudan, L., "Science at the Bar — Causes for Concern"; P.L. Quinn, "The Philosopher of Science as Expert Witness"; both in Ruse, M., editor, *But Is it Science?* pp. 351–355, Prometheus Books, Buffalo, NY, 1988, pp. 351–355, 367–385. Ruse was the philosopher of science who most influenced American judges that creation is 'unscientific', and Laudan and Quinn refute his fallacious arguments. But see also note 34.

22.  See Ben Stein's DVD *Expelled: No Intelligence Allowed* (2008), and Bergman, J., *Slaughter of the Dissidents*, Leafcutter Press 2008.

Evolution is promoted by its practitioners as more than mere science. Evolution is promulgated as an ideology, a secular religion—a full-fledged alternative to Christianity, with meaning and morality. I am an ardent evolutionist and an ex-Christian, but I must admit that in this one complaint—and Mr [*sic*—Dr] Gish is but one of many to make it—the literalists are absolutely right. Evolution is a religion. This was true of evolution in the beginning, and it is true of evolution still today.

... Evolution therefore came into being as a kind of secular ideology, an explicit substitute for Christianity.[23]

Both creationists and evolutionists accept the same facts of science, they just interpret them based on different frameworks. One interpretation is based on atheistic materialism, and the other is based on God's perfect, revealed Word.

---

23. Ruse, M., "How evolution became a religion: creationists correct?" *National Post*, pp. B1,B3,B7 May 13, 2000.

# Chapter 2

## Argument: Evolution is Compatible with Christian Religion

*Evolutionists say, 'Evolution is not necessarily antithetical to Christianity— science and religion just deal with different realms of knowledge.'*

Though the media love to attack *creation* as unscientific, they're too canny to appear blatantly anti-*Christian*. In fact, they typically downplay the rabidly atheistic faith of many leading evolutionists. The PBS series *Evolution,* for example, included several virulent atheists, such as Stephen Jay Gould and Eugenie Scott,[1] to speak on their program; but it breathed not a word about their strongly held religious views and open assaults on Christianity. Such outspoken atheism does not play well in religious America.

### Is Darwinism anti-Christian?

The opening episode of the *Evolution* series is aptly titled 'Darwin's Dangerous Idea', presumably inspired by Daniel Dennett's book of the same name. Dennett argues that Darwin should be ranked ahead of Newton and Einstein as a scientific genius, because he united the disparate world of purposelessness and meaninglessness with the world of purpose and meaning. *Evolution's* producers acknowledge that Darwin's idea posed a

---

1.   Batten, D., "A who's who of evolutionists," *Creation* **20**(1):32, 1997, creation.com/who.

'threat' to the established views of his day, but they omit Dennett's famous insight that Darwinism was 'universal acid', eating through every traditional idea, especially 'meaning coming from on high and being ordained from the top down'.[2] Presumably that would have alerted the Christian audience too soon.

## Annie's death and the problem of evil

PBS 1 dramatizes a turning point in the spiritual life of Charles Darwin—the sickness and death of his beloved daughter Annie (he lost two other children in childhood as well). Although the series does not spell it out, Darwin's biographer James Moore makes it clear that this tragedy destroyed the truth of Christianity in Darwin's mind. How could there be a good God if He allowed this to happen? Instead, Darwin decided that Annie was an unfortunate victim of the laws of nature, i.e. she lost the struggle for existence.

Annie's death raised serious questions about God's goodness, but the prevailing view of Darwin's day—that the Earth was old and had long been filled with death and violence—provided no adequate answers. Alas, this was the prevailing view in the Church of England as well. This placed fossils millions of years *before* Adam. This view entails that death and suffering were around for millions of years before Adam, and yet God called His acts of creation 'very good'. Such a view evidently didn't appeal to Darwin. It's sad that many church leaders today still promote theistic evolution (the belief that God divinely ordained evolution—the struggle for survival and death—as His method of creation) and progressive creation (the belief that the 'days' of Creation in Genesis 1 refer to long ages of death and suffering). Both of these compromise views[3] have the insuperable problem of allowing death before sin. However, the proponents of these views claim that they are *more* acceptable to unbelievers than the literal Genesis view, failing to realize that this battle was already

---

2.    Dennett, D., *Darwin's Dangerous Idea: Evolution and the Meanings of Life*, Simon & Schuster, 1995.

3.    See "Creation compromises: questions and answers," creation.com/compromise for more information.

lost in Darwin's day. Yet this didn't stop the Church of England even apologizing to Darwin in 2008.[4]

But the Bible is very clear the Earth has a 'young' age (i.e. about 6,000 years),[5] and the events described in Genesis 1–3 perfectly explain how God could be good and yet the Earth be filled with death and suffering. The Bible says that God created everything 'very good' (Genesis 1:31), whereas death is an intruder, called 'the last enemy' (1 Corinthians 15:26). God did *not* introduce death and suffering millions of years ago—as many church leaders were saying in Darwin's time—but instead, suffering was the direct result of Adam's sin (Genesis 2:17, 3:19; Romans 5:12–19, 8:20–22; 1 Corinthians 15:21–22). To any Bible believer, this truth entails that the fossil record—a record of death, disease and suffering—must date *after* Adam's sin.[6,7]

In the end, Darwin concluded that Christianity is a 'damnable doctrine' because his unbelieving father would be condemned to Hell, but of course the PBS episode doesn't mention this! It does, however, show Darwin's older brother Erasmus (named after their evolutionary grandfather) mocking hymn singing in church.

### Kenneth Miller—a good Christian and an evolutionist?

While PBS 1 attempted to mute Darwin's obvious anti-Christianity, it prominently featured Kenneth Miller, who claims to be 'an orthodox Catholic and an orthodox Darwinist'. He wrote a book, *Finding Darwin's God* (2000), an anti-creationist polemic, to try to reconcile God and evolution. Miller has had a long history of joining forces with leading humanists against Creation, and his book is full of straw-man arguments, misinformation and

4.  Sarfati, J., "Church of England apologises to Darwin: Anglican Church's neo-Chamberlainite appeasement of secularism," creation.com/Anglican, 20 September 2008.

5.  Freeman, T.R., "The Genesis 5 and 11 fluidity question," *JoC* **19**(2):83–90, 2005; Sarfati, J., "Biblical chronogenealogies," *JoC* **17**(3):14–18, 2003; creation.com/chronogenealogy.

6.  See Sarfati, J., "The Fall: a cosmic catastrophe: Hugh Ross's blunders on plant death in the Bible," *JoC* **19**(3):60–64, 2005; creation.com/plant_death.

7.  Lubenow, M.L., "Pre-Adamites, sin, death and human fossils," *JoC* **12**(2): 222–232, 1998.

outright deception.[8,9] The last sentences in his book are revealing: "What kind of God do I believe in? … I believe in Darwin's God." Since Darwin was anti-Christian, as shown above, this is not the God any Christian can believe in. But PBS 1 shows Miller attending Mass and taking communion, hoping that this show of outward religiosity will convince people who prefer outward appearances to inward convictions (cf. Matthew 23:25–28).

### Religion and science — 'non-overlapping magisteria'?

Despite Darwin's obvious anti-Christianity, evolutionists like to say that Darwin didn't intend to disparage ideas of God. In fact, PBS 1 quotes evolutionist Stephen Jay Gould saying so. This is consistent with Gould's widely publicized claims that religion and science are 'non-overlapping magisteria' (NOMA).[10] That is, science deals with facts of the real world, while religion deals with ethics, values, morals, and what it means to be human.

However, this is based on the philosophically fallacious 'fact-value distinction', and is really an anti-Christian claim. For example, the Resurrection of Christ is an essential 'value' of the Christian faith (1 Corinthians 15:12–19), but it must also be a *fact* of history to be of value—it had to pass the 'testable' Bible prophecy that the tomb would be empty on the third day; and it had to impinge on science by demonstrating the power of God over so-called 'natural laws' that dead bodies decay, and do not return to life. Christians should be aware that this is not only a theoretical argument about the anti-Christian implications of NOMA—Gould openly dismissed John's *historical* narrative of Jesus' post-Resurrection appearance to doubting Thomas as a 'moral tale'.[10]

---

8.  For a thorough refutation of Miller's book *Finding Darwin's God*, see Woodmorappe, J. and Sarfati, J., "Mutilating Miller," *JoC* **15**(3): 29–35, 2001, creation.com/miller. It's notable that the ardent antitheist Dawkins recommends his book to Christians.

9.  See also Woodmorappe, J., "Miller's meanderings: only the same bogus contentions" (A review of *Only a Theory: Evolution and the Battle for America's Soul* by Kenneth Miller, Viking Penguin, New York, 2008), *JoC* **23**(1):19–23, 2009, creation.com/miller2.

10. Gould, S.J., *Rocks of Ages: Science and Religion in the Fullness of Life*, Ballantyne, NY, 1999.

This NOMA distinction really teaches that religion is just in one's head, which seems to dull the senses of many Christians more than an overt declaration that Christianity is false. So NOMA is even more insidious.

Christians should not fall for this false distinction between facts and morality. Christ is the Lord of the universe, and the Bible is accurate on everything it touches, not just faith and morality, but history, science and geography also. So Christians should not give up any part of the 'real world' to those with a materialistic agenda—especially when atheists are happy to let their own faith influence their science by promoting evolution.

Gould's real anti-Christian sentiments are shown by his 1990 lecture at Victoria University of Wellington, New Zealand. The whole theme of his lecture was that Darwin deliberately tried to counter the argument from design, and Gould speculated that this was because FitzRoy had browbeaten him with this argument. Gould also addressed the popular notion that evolution can be reconciled with religion and purpose because evolution is supposedly 'progress'. Gould slammed this idea, saying that evolution was just a blind, purposeless struggle for existence.[11] It seems that science and 'God' are compatible only when trying to pacify concerned Christians, but at other times Gould makes it clear that there's no room for God, at least in the 'real world'. None other than Kenneth Miller, who was impressed by Gould's NOMA idea, when he saw documentation of Gould's true feelings about belief in God, conceded that creationists had a point when they accused Gould of double talk:

> Some wonder if Gould, in his heart, really believes these words. Late in 1997, Phillip Johnson described Gould's essay as 'a tissue of half-truths aimed at putting the religious people to sleep, or luring them into a "dialogue" on terms set by the materialists'. Had Johnson seen Gould on television a year later, his sense of Gould's duplicity might have

---

11. For an accurate account of Gould's lecture, see Wieland, C., "Darwin's real message: have you missed it?" *Creation* **14**(4):16–19, 1992, creation.com/realmessage.

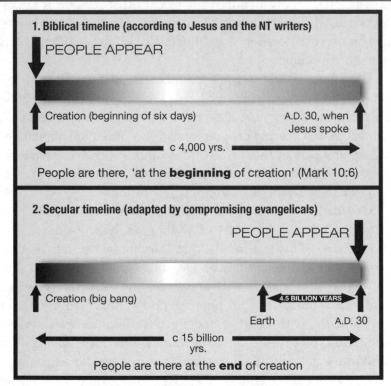

1. Biblical timeline (according to Jesus and the NT writers)

PEOPLE APPEAR

Creation (beginning of six days)  A.D. 30, when Jesus spoke

c 4,000 yrs.

People are there, 'at the **beginning** of creation' (Mark 10:6)

2. Secular timeline (adapted by compromising evangelicals)

PEOPLE APPEAR

Creation (big bang)  4.5 BILLION YEARS

Earth  A.D. 30

c 15 billion yrs.

People are there at the **end** of creation

## Jesus and the age of the world

The 'secular timeline', from an alleged 'big bang' to now, is accepted by most people in the evangelical Christian world, even though they would deny evolution. However, this puts people at the 'end' of creation (see diagram). But in several places in the Bible, the Lord Jesus Christ, the Creator made flesh, makes it plain that this is wrong—people were therefrom the beginning of creation. This means that the world cannot be billions of years old.

For example, dealing with the doctrine of marriage, Jesus says in **Mark 10:6**, 'But from the beginning of the creation, God made them male and female.'

In **Luke 11:50–51**, Jesus says:
> 'That the blood of all the prophets, which was shed from the foundation of the world, may be required of this generation; From the blood of Abel to the blood of Zacharias …'.

**Romans 1:20** makes it plain that people can clearly see God's power by looking at the 'things that are made', and that people have been able to see this 'from the creation of the world'. Not billions of years after creation.

been dramatically confirmed:

> INTERVIEWER: Gould disputes the religious claim that man is at the center of the universe. The idea of a science-religious dialogue, he says, is 'sweet' but unhelpful.
>
> [Speaking to Gould]: Why is it sweet?
>
> GOULD: Because it gives comfort to many people. I think that notion that we are all in the bosom of Abraham or are in God's embracing love is—look, it's a tough life and if you can delude yourself into thinking that there's all some warm and fuzzy meaning to it all, it's enormously comforting. But I do think it's just a story we tell ourselves.

Hard to see how something Gould regards as 'just a story we tell ourselves' could also be an obligatory step in 'the attainment of wisdom' (*Finding Darwin's God*, page 170).

On PBS 1, Stephen Jay Gould said that Darwinism answers who we are, as far as science can answer that question. Boston University biologist Chris Schneider said that evolution 'stirs the soul.' The series ends with a comment by Darwin's biographer, James Moore: 'Darwin's vision of nature was, I believe, fundamentally a religious vision.' In the light of this, it's amazing that the series persists in claiming that evolution is 'science' rather than 'religion.'

### Deep time—the truth seeps out

Despite cunning efforts to deceive people that evolution and Christianity are compatible, the truth eventually leaks out. Probably everyone has seen one of the cute illustrations that show man's tiny place on the 'yardstick of time.' In PBS 2, for example, Neil Shubin, a paleontologist from the University of Chicago, shares his version of the story. He claims that the Earth is 4.5 billion years old; and to show how insignificant humans are, he scales this time to one hour. Then he claims that animals existed only in the last 10 minutes, while humans appeared only in the last 100th of a second.

Despite the PBS series' claim to be respectful of Christianity, this is one of many examples of the direct contradiction between evolution/billions of years and Christ's teachings. Jesus says in Mark 10:6, 'But *from the beginning of the creation*, God made them male and female.' This statement is consistent with Christ's belief in a literal interpretation of Genesis, which teaches that the Earth was created about 4000 years before He spoke those words. Adam and Eve were created on Day 6, which on the scale of 4000 years is almost indistinguishable from the beginning.[12] But this time frame is diametrically opposed to Shubin's illustration, which has man appearing almost at the end, not the beginning.[13,14]

## What about God?

'What about God?' is the title of the final episode (7) in the PBS series on *Evolution*. To the very end, the producers tried to obscure the obvious—that evolution and biblical Christianity are diametrically opposed. Actually, they hardly discussed *biblical* Christianity, but interviewed people who believe that 'God' used evolution. As is typical of most evolutionists, they acknowledge biblical Christianity and even interview representatives of it, but they omit the strongest case of the best defenders, and give much airtime to those who haven't the faintest idea about defending biblical Christianity. But the PBS program was honest about one thing: it clearly showed examples of the baneful effects of compromise among Christians, and these incidents should raise alarms among pastors that they have an obligation to exhort their flock to

---

12. See also Sarfati, J., *Refuting Compromise*, ch. 9, 2004/2011 for further discussion of these passages.

13. There are also many scientific problems with any assertions that the Earth looks old. The conflicts between billions of years with the words of Christ and true science are well outlined in Wieland, C., "The earth: how old does it look?" *Creation* **23**(1):8–13, 2000, creation.com/earth_how_old.

14. See also Livingston, D., "Jesus Christ on the infallibility of Scripture," creation.com/jesus_bible, 6 April 2004.

be ready with answers, as the Apostle Peter commanded in 1 Peter 3:15.

## Concealing the truth about 'fundamentalist' concerns

The PBS narrator (Liam Neeson) talks about the views of 'Christian fundamentalists like Ken Ham' (president of *Answers in Genesis* in the US), but he never defines the word, of course. Presumably the producers hope to exploit modern connotations of the word, and their attempt at name-calling received an unexpected bonus after the 2001 terrorist attack against the United States, attributed to Muslim 'fundamentalists'. But this modern usage of the term reflects ignorance of its original honorable meaning:

> Historically, fundamentalism has been used to identify one holding to the five fundamentals of the faith adopted by the General Assembly of the Presbyterian Church of the USA in 1910. The five fundamentals were the miracles of Christ, the virgin birth of Christ, the substitutionary atonement of Christ, the bodily resurrection of Christ, and the inspiration of Scripture.[15]

The PBS narrator scornfully dismisses Mr Ham as one of those who teach a 'literal' interpretation of the creation accounts (*sic*—see below) in Genesis. This is a common tactic among evolutionists, who imply that there is something unusual about taking Genesis literally, but they completely ignore what 'fundamentalists' teach about interpreting historical narrative as historical narrative, interpreting poetry as poetry, and making distinctions between them.[16]

The Hebrew grammar of Genesis shows that Genesis 1–11 has the same literary style as Genesis 12–50, which no one doubts is historical narrative. For example, the early chapters of Genesis

---

15. Enns, Paul, *Moody Handbook of Theology*, p. 613, Moody Press, Chicago, 1989.

16. See Grigg, R., "Should Genesis Be Taken Literally?" *Creation* 16(1):38–41, 1993, creation.com/literal.

frequently use the construction called the 'waw consecutive', usually an indicator of historical sequence. Genesis 1–11 also has several other trademarks of historical narrative, such as 'accusative particles' that mark the objects of verbs, and terms that are often carefully defined. And the Hebrew verb grammar of Genesis 1 has a particular feature that fits *exactly* what would be expected if it were representing a series of past events. That is, only the first verb is perfect, while the verbs that continue the narrative are imperfect.[17] In Genesis 1, the first verb is *bara* (create) which is perfect, while the subsequent verbs that move the narrative forward are imperfect. But parallelisms, which are characteristic of Hebrew poetry, are absent from Genesis, except where people are cited, e.g. Genesis 4:23. If Genesis were truly poetic, it would use parallelisms throughout.[18,19]

The mention of 'creation accounts' is simply a hint at the defunct 'documentary hypothesis', which argued that Genesis was pieced together from several contradictory sources.[20] The charge of contradiction between Genesis 1 and 2 is amply resolved by noting that Genesis 1:1–2.4a is a summary outline of the whole creation, while Genesis 2:4b ff. focuses on the creation of male and female, so they are complementary rather than contradictory.[21]

In general, they wished to portray all objections to evolution as 'religious'. Of course, they had to ignore the many scientists who are creationists, as well as most of the founders of modern science.

---

17. *Gesenius' Hebrew grammar*, 2nd Ed., trans. Cowley, A.E., pp. 132–133, Oxford University Press, Oxford, 1910.

18. Kaiser, W.C. Jr., "The literary form of Genesis 1–11" in Payne, J.B., *New Perspectives on the Old Testament*, pp. 59–60, Word, Inc., Waco, Texas, USA, 1970.

19. After the first edition was published, I wrote *Refuting Compromise* (2004, 2011), a detailed defence of the plain meaning of Genesis against those who would read long-age ideas into the text, particularly Hugh Ross. It is far more detailed regarding these points.

20. The documentary hypothesis is amply refuted by Grigg, R., Did Moses really write Genesis? *Creation* **20**(4):43–46, 1998, creation.com/jedp.

21. See Batten, D., "Genesis Contradictions?" *Creation* **18**(4):44–45, 1996, creation.com/genesis-contradictions; creation.com/birkett#contradictions.

Specifically, these points blow most of the PBS program's 'evidence' sky high.

## Christian college compromise causes confusion!

The damage that evolution has caused on college campuses is legendary, and it's not difficult to cite examples of children from Christian homes who have turned away from their childhood faith after attending college—even 'Christian' college. The final episode of the PBS series gives a striking example from Wheaton College, which is said to be a conservative Christian college. According to Wheaton's website:

> Wheaton College selects candidates for admission from those who evidence a vital Christian experience, high academic ability, moral character, personal integrity, social concern, and the desire to pursue a liberal arts education as defined in the aims and objectives of the College.

This college is the show-pony of the PBS series, showing viewers how people can mix God and evolution. But one must wonder how the school defines a 'vital Christian experience' since their professors evidently don't believe the Bible, the only source of information about Christ. At one point in the PBS series, it shows a teacher on a school field trip who proclaims that a water hole is 33 million years old.

There was quite a stir back in 1961 when Prof. Walter Hearn promoted evolution at Wheaton. As a result of this controversy, now the school apparently insists that professors sign a statement that Adam was a historical figure.

But the PBS clips make it abundantly clear that this statement is a dead letter. If the professors themselves 'support' this apparent anti-evolution statement, they have no qualms about inviting visiting lecturers who don't believe the biblical account of Creation and even attack it.

One example is Keith Miller, who claimed on the PBS program to be an 'ardent evangelical Christian'. He asserted, without evidence, that there are lots of transitional forms. When questioned, he said that God chose Adam and Eve out of other humans that existed. This just shows that the word 'evangelical', like 'Christian', has become debased currency. At one time, it meant someone who believed the Reformation (and biblical) doctrines of the inerrancy and sufficiency of Scripture. This is not always so nowadays, and certainly doesn't apply to Miller.

Genesis 2:7 teaches that the first man was made from dust and *became* alive when God breathed the breath of life into him. This rules out the idea that Adam was *already* a living primate of some kind when God breathed on him. Eve was made from Adam's rib (Genesis 2:21–24). Luke's genealogy of Christ traces His lineage (through Mary) all the way back to Adam, then directly to God, not via any ape-like creatures or pond scum (Luke 3:23–38). Further, 1 Corinthians 15:45 states that Adam was the 'first man', and Eve was so named because she was to become the 'mother of all living' (Genesis 3:20). Also, Paul's teachings about male and female roles in 1 Corinthians 11:8–9 and 1 Timothy 2:13–14 explicitly support the historical order of creation in Genesis 2:21–23.[22,23]

The sad thing about Wheaton is the admission—shown on the final PBS episode—that most people become *more* confused about their Christian faith while they attend this 'Christian' college. The students wonder whether there's a place for God if evolution is true, and rightly so.[24]

This confusion should hardly be surprising—Billy Graham's former colleague Charles Templeton totally apostatized after attending the compromising Princeton Theological Seminary.[25] *Creation Ministries International* has received several testimonies from people who were shipwrecked in their faith by compromising 'Christians' but later restored with the help of CMI and other

---

22. See Sarfati, J., "Genesis: Bible authors believed it to be history," *Creation* **28**(2):21–23, 2006; creation.com/gen-hist.

23. Cosner, L., "The Use of Genesis in the New Testament," *Creation* **33**(2):16-19, 2011; creation.com/nt.

24. See Woodmorappe, John, "The horse and the tractor: Why God and evolution don't mix," *Creation* **22**(4):53, 2000, creation.com/horsetractor.

25. See Wieland, C., "Death of an apostate," *Creation* **25**(1):6, 2002, creation.com/templeton-death.

Christian ministries that present a consistently biblical approach to origins.[26]

## Seeds of apostasy

In contrast to the claims of evolutionists, evolution is a direct assault on the authority of Scripture, and it is the seed of most modern apostasy. Exhibit A is Nathan Baird, a geology major who stars on the final PBS episode. He had a creationist upbringing, sort of, but now from his lofty height at Wheaton he proclaims that most Christians dismiss evolution because they don't understand it. Now he thinks that God used the big bang and evolution, and infused a spirit supernaturally into some humans. He proclaimed: 'God is bigger than the box I've put him in.'

This slogan is hardly original to Nathan. Rank apostates like retired Episcopal Bishop John Shelby Spong[27] also spout such vacuous tripe. But creationists don't put God into any box; rather, they are humble enough to *believe what God has revealed about Himself in the Bible*, including when and how He created. It's people like Nathan who put God into a box of their own making, by presuming that God would not have intervened in His creation in a different way from the way He currently upholds it (Col. 1:16–17, Hebrews 1:3, passages referring to Christ, the God-man). They also, in effect, presume that God was unable to communicate in clear language about the history of the universe.

## Lack of apologetics

Nathan's upbringing is sadly typical of the lack of apologetics teaching—how to defend the faith—in the churches. The term 'Christian apologetics' doesn't refer to apologizing (or saying 'sorry') for being a Christian. The confusion arises because the English word *apology* now has a rather different meaning from the Greek word from which it was derived: ἀπολογία (*apología*).

---

26. E.g. "Sonia's Testimony: Creation magazine opened my eyes to the Gospel!", creation.com/Sonia; "A testimony: Joel Galvin," creation.com/galvin; and "No excuse to disbelieve: Lita Cosner," creation.com/lita.

27. See Bott, M. and Sarfati, J., "What's wrong with Bishop Spong," *Apologia* 4(1):3–27, 1995, creation.com/spong.

The latter meant *defence*. The Greek term comes from words meaning 'out of logic/reason', so refers to a reasoned defence that would be given in a court of law. The classic example is Plato's *Apology*, Socrates' defence against the charges of atheism and corrupting the youth.

Christian apologetics is the reasoned defence of the Christian faith against objections, but also includes the setting forth of positive grounds for Christianity. It is the duty of all Christians, because:

- The Lord Jesus Christ commanded: 'Love the Lord your God … with all your *mind*.' (Matthew 22:37)

- The Apostle Peter commanded Christians: 'Always be prepared to *give an answer* to everyone who asks you to *give the reason* for the hope that you have.' (1 Peter 3:15)

- Jude's inspired epistle said: 'I found it necessary to write to you exhorting you to *contend earnestly for the faith* which was once for all delivered to the saints.' (v. 3)

- The Apostle Paul said: 'We *demolish arguments* and every pretension that sets itself up against the knowledge of God, and we *take captive every thought* to make it obedient to Christ' (2 Corinthians 10:5).

Many Christians have no idea how to defend their faith. The most serious problem is that parents do not have answers to their children's questions.[28] But as the Christian criminology professor Mike S. Adams said:

> If Christianity dies in America it will not be for a lack of evidence of its truthfulness. It will be for a lack of dissemination of the evidence of its truthfulness. …

> An emotional experience can cause someone to find God. It can also cause someone who previously found God to move closer toward Him. But emotion is not enough. There must be a strong intellectual

---

28. Cosner, L., "Who has an answer?" 27 August 2009, creation.com/answer.

underpinning to one's faith. That intellectual underpinning is not only needed to strengthen a man's faith. It is needed to help him share it with others.[29]

PBS 7 showed Nathan's family outside having lunch. Nathan's father correctly believed that evolution was a frontal assault on Genesis 1 and his son's faith, but he didn't seem very well informed about the issues (or else his most telling arguments were edited out). Nathan's father couldn't answer some of his son's facile arguments, and he asked Nathan's mother to bail him out.

Nathan's mother correctly pointed out that unwavering adherence to the Bible was a common factor in church growth. She also recounted the advice of a friend: 'Don't send Nathan to Wheaton—it could destroy his faith.' One might argue whether a person who 'loses his/her faith' truly had saving faith to begin with (1 John 2:19), but this incident shows that Wheaton had a reputation for undermining students' faith. It's a shame that Nathan's mother didn't follow this advice before forking out a fortune to a college that doesn't teach what it claims. The money may as well be spent on a secular college, because at least their students know what to expect. It's fortunate for Wheaton and many other 'Christian' colleges that they can't be sued for false advertising.

Darwinian evolution truly was a 'dangerous idea,' one that consciously undermined faith in God and belief in the Bible, replacing it with scepticism and a materialist worldview. It's the height of hypocrisy for atheists like Gould to claim that evolution is 'compatible' with Christianity.[30] (See also pages 168–170 ff.)

---

29. Both from townhall.com/columnists/MikeAdams/, 2010.

30. See response to this section, "Wheaton College Student Objects!," 15 October 2001, creation.com/wheaton-college-student-objects.

# Chapter 3

# Argument: Evolution is *True* Science, Not "Just a Theory"

*Evolutionists say, 'Evolution is real science*
*that solves real problems; it is founded on*
*the modern belief that we should try to*
*explain the universe in natural terms.'*

E volutionists bristle at the accusation that evolution is 'just a theory', not a fact.  Indeed, this is the very first example of 'creationist nonsense' that *Scientific American* lists and answers in its '15 Answers to Creationist Nonsense':

### 1. Evolution is only a theory.  It is not a fact or a scientific law.

All sciences frequently rely on indirect evidence. Physicists cannot see subatomic particles directly, for instance, so they verify their existence by watching for telltale tracks that the particles leave in cloud chambers.  The absence of direct observation does not make physicists' conclusions less certain. [*SA* 79]

Unfortunately, some creationists actually do argue that 'evolution is just a theory'.  What they usually *mean* is 'Evolution is not proven fact, so it should not be promoted dogmatically.' (Therefore that is what they *should* say.) The problem with using the word 'theory' in this case is that scientists use it to mean a well-substantiated explanation of data.  This includes well-known

49

ones such as Einstein's Theory of Relativity and Newton's Theory of Gravity, and lesser-known ones such as the Debye–Hückel Theory of electrolyte solutions and the Deryagin–Landau/Verwey–Overbeek (DLVO) theory of the stability of lyophobic sols, etc. It would be better to say that particles-to-people evolution is an unsubstantiated *hypothesis* or *conjecture* (see also Appendix 2, page 235).

*Scientific American*'s comments about the scientific study of subatomic particles, however, miss the point—these cloud chamber experiments are still *observations* in the *present* and are *repeatable.* A dinosaur turning into a bird 150 million years ago is neither observable in real time, directly or indirectly, nor repeatable. Chapter 1 of this book explained this confusion about the difference between 'operational science' and 'origins science' (see page 22–26).

## What is science? What is a theory?

*Scientific American* devoted the first *five* points of its article on 'creationist nonsense' to defending evolution against charges that it's not good science. In this chapter I'll look at each in turn, but first it's absolutely essential to define terms carefully. How can you know whether something is 'true science' or 'just a theory', unless you know what these terms mean? Yet evolutionists often make sweeping claims without adequately defining their terms.

The sixteenth-century philosopher Sir Francis Bacon, considered the founder of the scientific method, gave a pretty straightforward definition of science:

observation → induction → hypothesis → test hypothesis by experiment → proof/disproof → knowledge

This view of science, however, depends on two major philosophical assumptions: causality and induction, which must be accepted by faith. Many modern scientists are so ignorant of basic philosophy that they don't even realize that they have made these assumptions, although several philosophers, such as David Hume and Bertrand Russell, have pointed it out.[1]

The editors of *Scientific American* and other leading

1. Batten, D., "It's not science," 28 February 2002, creation.com/its-not-science.

evolutionists define 'science' in a self-serving way that excludes God and His Word. They openly equate science with the philosophy of 'methological naturalism'—as has already been shown—'to explain the universe purely in terms of observed or testable natural mechanisms' [*SA* 85].

The prominent evolutionary biologist Richard Lewontin has spoken bluntly about this anti-God, materialistic bias:

> We take the side of science *in spite* of the patent absurdity of some of its constructs, *in spite* of its failure to fulfil many of its extravagant promises of health and life, *in spite* of the tolerance of the scientific community for unsubstantiated just-so stories, because we have a prior commitment, a commitment to materialism. It is not that the methods and institutions of science somehow compel us to accept a material explanation of the phenomenal world, but, on the contrary, that we are forced by our *a priori* adherence to material causes to create an apparatus of investigation and a set of concepts that produce material explanations, no matter how counter-intuitive, no matter how mystifying to the uninitiated. Moreover, that materialism is an absolute, for we cannot allow a Divine Foot in the door.[2]

Most people think that 'science' follows the evidence wherever it leads. But it is impossible to avoid letting our worldview color our interpretation of the facts. Creationists are honest about the philosophical basis behind their interpretation, whereas naturalists often pretend that they don't operate from any philosophical bias. The late atheist Stephen Jay Gould, unlike many of his peers, was candid about this bias:

> Our ways of learning about the world are strongly influenced by the social preconceptions and biased modes of thinking that each scientist must apply to any problem. The stereotype of a fully rational and objective "scientific method", with individual scientists as logical

---

2.  Lewontin, R., "Billions and billions of demons," *The New York Review*, January 9, 1997, p. 31, creation.com/lewontin.

(and interchangeable) robots is self-serving mythology.[3]

The philosopher of science David Hull had earlier noted:

> ... science is not as empirical as many scientists seem to think it is. Unobserved and even unobservable entities play an important part in it. Science is not just the making of observations: it is the making of inferences on the basis of observations within the framework of a theory.[4]

Dr Scott Todd, an immunologist at Kansas State University was candid about how certain conclusions would be avoided at all costs, regardless of the evidence:

> Even if all the data point to an intelligent designer, such an hypothesis is excluded from science because it is not naturalistic.[5]

IMPO ## What is evolution?

It is vitally important that words such as 'evolution' be used accurately and consistently. The theory of 'evolution' that the evolutionists are really promoting, and which creationists oppose, is the idea that particles turned into people over time, without any need for an intelligent designer. The evolutionist Kerkut accurately defined this 'General Theory of Evolution' (GTE) as 'the theory that all the living forms in the world have arisen from a single source which itself came from an inorganic form.' He continued: 'the evidence which supports this is not sufficiently strong to allow us to consider it as anything more than a working hypothesis.'[6]

However, many evolutionary propagandists are guilty of the deceitful practice of *equivocation*, that is, switching the meaning

---

3. Gould, S.J., *Natural History* **103**(2):14, 1994.

4. Hull, D., "The effect of essentialism on taxonomy—two thousand years of stasis (II)". *British Journal for the Philosophy of Science* **16**(61):1–18, 1965.

5. Todd, S.C., correspondence to *Nature* **410**(6752):423, 30 Sept. 1999, creation.com/todd.

6. Kerkut, G.A., *Implications of Evolution*, Pergamon, Oxford, UK, p. 157, 1960.

of a single word (evolution) part-way through an argument. A common tactic, 'bait-and-switch', is simply to produce examples of change over time, call this 'evolution', then imply that the GTE is thereby proven or even essential, and Creation disproved. The PBS *Evolution* series and *Scientific American* are full of examples of this fallacy.

## Information — the real problem with evolution

The main scientific objection to the GTE is *not* that changes occur through time, and neither is it about the *size* of the change (so I would discourage use of the terms micro- and macro-evolution—see Appendix 2, page 238). The key issue is the *type* of change required—to change microbes into men requires changes that *increase the genetic information content.* The three billion DNA 'letters' stored in each human cell nucleus convey a great deal more information (known as 'specified complexity') than the over half a million DNA 'letters' of the 'simplest' self-reproducing organism. The DNA sequences in a 'higher' organism, such as a human being or a horse, for instance, code for structures and functions unknown in the sort of 'primitive first cell' from which all other organisms are said to have evolved.

None of the alleged proofs of 'evolution in action' provide a *single* example of functional new information being added to genes. Rather, they all involve sorting and loss of information. To claim that mere change proves that information-*increasing* change can occur is like saying that because a merchant can sell goods, he can sell them for a profit. The origin of information is a major problem for the GTE.[7] 'Information theory', as it is called, is a whole new branch of science that has effectively destroyed the last underpinnings of evolution—explained fully in the monumental work *In the Beginning was Information by* Dr Werner Gitt, professor and head of the Department of Information Technology at the German Federal Institute of Physics and Technology.

The second episode of the PBS *Evolution* series, titled 'Great

---

7.    See Wieland, C., "Beetle Bloopers," *Creation* **19**(3):30, 1997, creation.com/beetle; and Grigg, R., "Information: A modern scientific design argument," *Creation* **22**(2):50–53, 2000.

Transformations,' faced this problem when it tried to prove the 'big picture' of evolution, i.e. the 'General Theory of Evolution'. Of course, it could offer no experimental evidence, only inference. Its only experimental 'evidence' for 'evolution' was a bunch of examples of biological change that don't increase information content, and so actually these examples have nothing to do with the 'big picture'.

The PBS program did make a revealing comment about the real nature of the 'evidence' for evolution: 'The evidence for evolution is all around us, if we choose to look for it.' The comment is revealing, not because the evidence really supports evolution, but because the narrator inadvertently makes an important point. That is, creationists and evolutionists have the same evidence ('facts'), but we interpret it differently because of our different axioms (starting assumptions). In reality, evolutionists have a materialistic bias, which rejects a common designer *a priori* (see Lewontin's admission on page 51), and this applies even to evolutionists who believe in 'God'. Because of their bias, evolutionists interpret *any* facts as evidence for evolution. This would probably explain why a lot of the science in the PBS series was not even directly stated as evidence for evolution, but is shown as if it is. It also explains why fragmentary remains are interpreted as important 'transitional forms'. Conversely, creationists do *not* dispute the facts, since we have the same facts, although we frequently dispute assertions *claimed* to be facts when they are certainly not!

The PBS narrator blindly asserts that all living organisms come from a single source and that we can now trace branches and roots. Yet the series utterly fails to explain one of the most vexing problems with evolution: how non-living chemicals could form a living cell by time and chance, despite the insuperable chemical hurdles (see pages 157 ff.).[8] Interestingly, the PBS producer Richard Hutton never acknowledged this problem in

---

8.    See also Thaxton, C.B., Bradley, W.L. and Olsen, R L., 1984. *The Mystery of Life's Origin*, Philosophical Library Inc., New York; and "Origin of life questions and answers", creation.com/origin.

the series, but he did on a *Washington Post* online forum,[9] when he answered the question 'What are some of the larger questions which are still unanswered by evolutionary theory?'

> There are open questions and controversies, and the fights can be fierce. Just a few of them:
>
> The origin of life. There is no consensus at all here—lots of theories, little science. That's one of the reasons we didn't cover it in the series. The evidence wasn't very good. ...

No, the evidence for the first living organism certainly isn't 'very good', but of course the producer wouldn't want his viewers to know that! In other words, the very roots of the alleged evolutionary tree are in very bad shape. So they gloss over the problems, assert that there really is a well-documented tree, and then move on to find similarities between organisms and claim that this proves a common ancestor.

## Swatting at gnats

Instead of properly defining evolution or addressing the key scientific problem with evolution—i.e. the miraculous appearance of new genetic information from nothing—evolutionists swat at gnats and swallow camels. Just look at the second and third examples of 'creationist nonsense' in *Scientific American*'s '15 Answers to Creationist Nonsense'. Both of them miss the point.

> ### 2. Natural selection is based on circular reasoning: the fittest are those who survive, and those who survive are deemed fittest. [SA 79]
>
> Like the creationist argument that evolution is 'just a theory', this is another argument that *Creation Ministries International* has previously advised creationists not to use (see Appendix 2, page 219).

---

9.  http://discuss.washingtonpost.com/wp-srv/zforum/01/
    evolution2_092601.htm, last downloaded 14 October 2010.

*[handwritten annotation: "* SAYING OF THE SAME THIN TWICE OVER IN DIFFERENT WORDS"]*

Why should we argue this, since tautology is quite common in science? Moreover, as will be shown in detail in the next chapter, natural selection is *not* evidence of evolution. In fact, it is an important part of the Creation/Fall framework!

### 3. Evolution is unscientific, because it is not testable or falsifiable. It makes claims about events that were not observed and can never be re-created.

This blanket dismissal of evolution ignores important distinctions that divide the field into at least two broad areas: microevolution and macroevolution. Microevolution looks at changes within species over time—changes that may be preludes to speciation, the origin of new species. Macroevolution studies how taxonomic groups above the level of species change. Its evidence draws frequently from the fossil record and DNA comparisons to reconstruct how various organisms may be related. [*SA* 80]

Look who's talking about 'ignoring important distinctions'! It's evolutionary propagandists who generally mix them up. Biologists frequently define evolution as 'change in gene frequency with time' or 'descent with modification', or other such '*micro*evolution' words, and then cite insignificant examples of change within species, such as Darwin's finches, as clinching proof of 'evolution' in the '*macro*' sense and disproof of creationism! An example is Eugenie Scott, who approvingly cited a teacher whose pupils said after her 'definition', '*Of course* species change with time! You mean that's evolution?!'[10] Indeed, evolutionists encourage such deception, as long as it results in children learning evolution.[11]

---

10. Scott, E., "Dealing with anti-evolutionism," *Reports of the National Center for Science Education*, **17**(4):24–28, 1997; quote on p. 26, with emphasis in original.

11. Sarfati, J., "Evolutionist: it's ok to deceive students to teach evolution," creation.com/deceive, 24 September 2008.

## Glossing over the absence of evidence

With such verbal sleights of hand, evolutionists gloss over their complete lack of evidence for so-called 'macro-evolution.' Their supposed 'evidence' doesn't speak for itself; it must be *interpreted.* As John Rennie admitted in *Scientific American,* this evidence is interpreted within a materialistic framework. Ironically, materialists turn around and proclaim evolution as a major evidence for materialism, even though their materialistic framework was responsible for this viewpoint in the first place! Creationists interpret the same evidence but by a biblical framework, and they reach opposite conclusions.[12]

Another supposed 'evidence' that evolution makes good science is its ability to make 'predictions about future discoveries,' such as the discovery of 'a succession of hominid creatures with features progressively less apelike and more modern.'[13] *Scientific American* makes this very claim.

> In the historical sciences (which include astronomy, geology and archaeology, as well as evolutionary biology), hypotheses can still be tested by checking whether they accord with physical evidence and whether they lead to verifiable predictions about future discoveries. For instance, evolution implies that between the earliest-known ancestors of humans (roughly five million years old) and the appearance of anatomically modern humans (about 100,000 years ago), one should find a succession of hominid creatures with features progressively less apelike and more modern, which is indeed what the fossil record shows. ... Evolutionary biology [also] routinely makes predictions far more refined and precise than this, and researchers test them constantly. [*SA* 80]

Given such flimsy evidence for the scientific integrity of evolution, what 'evidence' would be required to disprove evolution

---

12. See Sarfati, J., "Presuppositionalism vs evidentialism, and is the human genome simple?" creation.com/presupp, 6 June 2005.

13. The false claim of transitional forms between apes and humans is discussed in chapter 12.

(an especially difficult task, because it is impossible to 'disprove' a philosophical assumption)? *Scientific American* tries, anyway.

> Evolution could be disproved in other ways, too. If we could document the spontaneous generation of just one complex life-form from inanimate matter, then at least a few creatures seen in the fossil record might have originated this way. If superintelligent aliens appeared and claimed credit for creating life on earth (or even particular species), the purely evolutionary explanation would be cast in doubt. But no one has yet produced such evidence. [*SA* 80]

None of this would 'disprove evolution', since big-picture evolution is really just a grab-bag of ideas about naturalistic (Godless) origins. Evolutionists already believe in spontaneous generation, but now call it 'chemical evolution'. In fact, some scientists are trying to create life from non-living chemicals in an attempt to show that it is possible for life to arise spontaneously.[14] They would actually be *delighted* if any or multiple examples of spontaneous generation were documented, because it would vindicate their belief that life came into being without an intelligent Creator. It would also solve their problem with the DNA in microbes, which does not show a pattern consistent with the presumption that it shares a common ancestry with other forms of life. To solve this vexing problem, multiple spontaneous origins have already been proposed, without any suggestion that this would 'disprove evolution'.[15]

The Bible claims to be a revelation by the Creator of life and the Universe, who certainly has 'claimed credit for creating life on Earth', yet *Scientific American* editor John Rennie does not see this as casting doubt on evolution. And there is excellent historical, archaeological and textual evidence that the Bible's claims are true.[16] But Rennie has apparently already made up his mind that

---

14. See J. Sarfati, "Synthetic life by Venter?", 25 May 2010, creation.com/venter.

15. Barnett, A., "The second coming. Did life evolve on Earth more than once?" New Scientist **157**(2121):19, 1998.

16. See "Bible questions and answers," creation.com/bible.

this evidence doesn't exist—this would presumably upset his materialistic faith. He goes on to say,

> It should be noted that the idea of falsifiability as the defining characteristic of science originated with philosopher Karl Popper in the 1930s. More recent elaborations on his thinking have expanded the narrowest interpretation of his principle precisely because it would eliminate too many branches of clearly scientific endeavor. [*SA* 80]

This is simply an attempt to immunize evolution from the same criticism that is advanced against creationists. As is often pointed out, it's hard to come up with a definition of 'science' that includes evolution and excludes creation unless it's blatantly self-serving.

## A 'good theory' because it's 'widely accepted'?

One of the most absurd, self-serving criteria that evolutionists give for a good scientific theory is that most published scientists accept the theory as valid. This is the basis for *Scientific American*'s next attack on 'creationist nonsense':

### 4. Increasingly, scientists doubt the truth of evolution.

> No evidence suggests that evolution is losing adherents. Pick up any issue of a peer-reviewed biological journal, and you will find articles that support and extend evolutionary studies or that embrace evolution as a fundamental concept.

> Conversely, serious scientific publications disputing evolution are all but nonexistent. In the mid-1990s George W. Gilchrist of the University of Washington surveyed thousands of journals in the primary literature, seeking articles on intelligent design or creation science. Among those hundreds of thousands of scientific reports, he found none. In the past two years, surveys done independently by Barbara Forrest of Southeastern Louisiana University and Lawrence

M. Krauss of Case Western Reserve University have been similarly fruitless. [*SA* 80]

It's logically possible for a belief to lose adherents even if journals still publish articles supporting this belief. Scientists who base such wild claims on a review of journals might benefit from some study of simple logic.[17]

Do they even know what to look for? Creationists are hardly likely to want to blow their cover and risk the discrimination epitomized by *Scientific American* (see page 9). Would *Nature* or *Science*, for example, ever knowingly publish a paper favourable to creation? Hardly. But in spite of the bias against such publication, creationist scientists have managed to publish papers when the creationist implications are disguised subtly enough. This shows that they *do* carry out real scientific research. Yet '15 Answers to Creationist Nonsense' has the audacity to claim,[18]

Creationists retort that a closed-minded scientific community rejects their evidence. Yet according to the editors of *Nature, Science* and other leading journals, few antievolution manuscripts are even submitted. [*SA* 80]

An absolutely amazing comment coming from a journal that's publicly reached the nadir of anti-creationist censorship and discrimination!

There is clear proof of censorship by *Scientific American*, *Science* and *Australasian Science*, where they have even denied creationists the normal courtesy of the right of reply. So why would scientists bother to waste their time? They know that their papers will be rejected, no matter how good the research, which explains why creationist scientists have, years ago, commenced their own peer-reviewed journals.[19]

---

17.  E.g. see Sarfati, J., "Loving God with all your mind: logic and creation," *JoC* **12**(2):142–151, 1998; creation.com/logic; DVD *Leaving Your Brains at the Church Door? The power of logic in defending your faith*, 2009.

18.  Examples are listed in Buckna, D., "Do creationists publish in notable refereed journals?," creation.com/creationpub.

19.  See Kulikovsky, A., "Creationism, science and peer review," *JoC* **22**(1):44-49 2008, creation.com/peer.

*Scientific American* acknowledges the credentials of some creationists, but not the fanatical censorship that they face.

> Some antievolution authors have published papers in serious journals. Those papers, however, rarely attack evolution directly or advance creationist arguments; at best, they identify certain evolutionary problems as unsolved and difficult (which no one disputes).

An interesting admission, but that's hardly the impression that evolutionists usually give to the public.

> In short, creationists are not giving the scientific world good reason to take them seriously. [*SA* 80]

So why does *Scientific American* take us seriously by writing this article?

## 'Disagreements aren't doubts about evolution'—doubletalk

*Scientific American*'s next example of supposed 'creationist nonsense' turns out to be doubletalk, and merely closes ranks against creationists. It repeats the old trick of claiming 'there is no doubt that evolution occurred; the only disagreement is about the mechanism.'

### 5. *The disagreements among even evolutionary biologists show how little solid science supports evolution.*

> Evolutionary biologists passionately debate diverse topics: how speciation happens, the rates of evolutionary change, the ancestral relationships of birds and dinosaurs, whether Neandertals were a species apart from modern humans, and much more. These disputes are like those found in all other branches of science. Acceptance of evolution as a factual occurrence and a guiding principle is nonetheless universal in biology. [*SA* 81]

This rhetorical flourish notwithstanding, modern evolutionary theory is *all about* providing a plausible mechanism for explaining life's complexity without God. If the disputes undermine all the favored mechanisms for evolution, then the whole materialist apologetic crumbles. When the supporters of various evolutionary camps score mortal blows against the mechanisms proposed by their rival camps, it's perfectly reasonable for creationists to point this out.

For example, with the origin of birds, there are two main theories: that birds evolved 'ground up' from running dinosaurs (the *cursorial* theory), and that they evolved 'trees-down' from small reptiles (the *arboreal* theory).[20] Both sides produce devastating arguments against the other side. The evidence indicates that the critics are *both* right—birds did not evolve either from running dinosaurs or from tree-dwelling mini-crocodiles. In fact, birds did not evolve from non-birds at all!

Similarly, supporters of 'jerky' evolution (*saltationism* and its relative, *punctuated equilibria*) point out that the fossil record does not show gradualism, and that the hypothetical transitional forms would be disadvantageous. But supporters of gradual evolution point out that sudden, large, information-increasing change is so improbable that one would need to invoke a secular 'miracle'. Creationists agree with both sides: punctuated evolution can't happen, and gradual evolution can't happen—in fact, particles-to-people evolution can't happen at all!

Lacking sound arguments, *Scientific American* stoops to quipping,

> Unfortunately, dishonest creationists have shown a
> willingness to take scientists' comments out of context
> to exaggerate and distort the disagreements. [*SA* 81]

Pure assertion. This 'quoting out of context' assertion is a common misrepresentation repeated by skeptics and their church allies; every quote by definition is 'out of context'—otherwise one would have to quote the entire work, i.e., the context. An even

---

20. Bergman, J., "The evolution of feathers: a major problem for Darwinism," *JoC* **17**(1):33–41, 2003, creation.com/feather.

sillier thing is to write to an author and ask whether he had been misquoted, which some anti-creationists actually do, as surprising as it may seem. All one needs to do to demonstrate misquoting is to compare the quote with the original.

The most frequently cited example of creationists 'misquoting' an avid evolutionist is their handling of Gould's punctuated equilibrium model. *Scientific American* says:

> Anyone acquainted with the works of paleontologist Stephen Jay Gould of Harvard University knows that in addition to co-authoring the punctuated-equilibrium model, Gould was one of the most eloquent defenders and articulators of evolution. (Punctuated equilibrium explains patterns in the fossil record by suggesting that most evolutionary changes occur within geologically brief intervals—which may nonetheless amount to hundreds of generations.) Yet creationists delight in dissecting out phrases from Gould's voluminous prose to make him sound as though he had doubted evolution, ... [*SA* 81]

Creationists do no such thing. Rather, they make it very clear that Gould was a staunch evolutionist but he criticized many aspects of neo-Darwinian theory. Quoting Gould is the perfectly honorable strategy of using a hostile witness.[21]

Yet *Scientific American* continues the misrepresentation of creationist claims:

> ... and they present punctuated equilibrium as though it allows new species to materialize overnight or birds to be born from reptile eggs. [*SA* 81]

First, most creationists present Gould's ideas correctly, and those ideas are not the exclusive property of evolutionists. Second, even many evolutionists think that Gould has largely himself to blame because of his injudicious (from an evolutionary viewpoint) comments. For example, Richard Goldschmidt was famous for promoting a 'hopeful monster' theory, which indeed said something very much like a bird hatching from a reptile

21. See Batten, Don, "Did creationists 'hijack' Gould's idea?" *JoC* **16**(2):22–24, 2002; creation.com/gould-hijack.

egg. And Gould wrote an article called 'The return of hopeful monsters' which said:

> I do, however, predict that during the next decade Goldschmidt will be largely vindicated in the world of evolutionary biology.[22]

If there is any 'out-of-context' quote in any books or articles written by me or my colleagues, we would like to know about it, because we are not about misleading people. Where such things have very rarely occurred in our literature over the years, we have willingly corrected them. *Scientific American* ends this discussion of this type of 'creationist nonsense' with yet another sweeping assertion, but without substance.

> When confronted with a quotation from a scientific authority that seems to question evolution, insist on seeing the statement in context. Almost invariably, the attack on evolution will prove illusory. [*SA* 81]

In reality, experience shows that when confronted by an accusation against creation or creationists by any scientific 'authority' one should insist on seeing documentation. Almost invariably, the attack on creation will prove illusory.

## Elephant hurling

There is a debate tactic known as 'elephant hurling'. This occurs when the critic throws summary arguments about complex issues to give the impression of weighty evidence, but with an unstated presumption that a large complex of underlying ideas is true, and failing to consider opposing data, usually because they have uncritically accepted the arguments from their own side. But we should challenge elephant-hurlers to offer *specifics* and challenge the *underlying assumptions*.

John Rennie's article on '15 Answers to Creationist Nonsense' opens with a classic example of elephant hurling.

---

22. Gould, S.J., "The return of hopeful monsters," *Natural History* **86**(6):22–30, 1977.

> When Charles Darwin introduced the theory of evolution through natural selection 143 years ago, the scientists of the day argued over it fiercely, but the massing evidence from paleontology, genetics, zoology, molecular biology and other fields gradually established evolution's truth beyond reasonable doubt. Today that battle has been won everywhere—except in the public imagination. [*SA* 78]

It is true that Darwin faced intense opposition when he introduced evolution. But his main opposition came from the *scientists*[23] and much of his support came from compromising clergymen, such as Rev. Charles Kingsley, who applied it to humans to assert that the African-Americans and Australian Aborigines had not evolved enough to understand the Gospel.[24]

To be honest, I think *Scientific American* underestimates the hold of evolution on the 'public imagination.' While many Americans say they believe in creation and reject evolution, sadly many seem to be 'evolutionized' in their thinking. This is shown by the widespread idea that their personal faith should not influence their public life. It's unfortunate to hear professing Christians who say that they won't let their faith influence their public policy, e.g. 'I'm personally opposed to abortion, but I won't enforce my faith on the pregnant woman who must be given the right to choose', although the unborn baby has no 'choice.' However, atheists are very happy to let their own faith influence their public policy and enforce their views on people—we rarely hear: "I'm personally in favor of abortion, but I won't enforce my view on the innocent unborn baby."[25]

---

23. See Foard, J., "Holy War? Who really opposed Darwin?" *Creation* **21**(4):26–27, 1999, creation.com/holy-war.

24. See Grigg, R., "Darwin's quisling," *Creation* **22**(1):50–51, 1999, creation.com/kingsley.

25. The related fallacy that 'you cannot/should not legislate morality' has been refuted in many articles, such as Bauman, Michael, "Dispelling false notions of the First Amendment: The Falsity, Futility, Folly Of Separating Morality From Law," equip.org/articles/law-and-morality, Christian Research Institute, last accessed 14 October 2010.

For this reason, the primary focus of Christian apologetics ministries like *Creation Ministries International* is not on refuting evolution *per se*, which by itself will accomplish little to change lives and opinions, but rather, building a consistent biblical Christian worldview. Refuting evolution (and millions of years) is a *corollary* of defending biblical truth.

*Scientific American*'s 'elephant hurling' continues with a repeat of common *ad hominem* attacks on the intelligence of creationists and their imagined threat to the advances of 'modern science' (as evolution is claimed to be):

> Embarrassingly, in the 21st century, in the most scientifically advanced nation the world has ever known, creationists can still persuade politicians, judges and ordinary citizens that evolution is a flawed, poorly supported fantasy. They lobby for creationist ideas such as 'intelligent design' to be taught as alternatives to evolution in science classrooms. [*SA* 78]

Perhaps the United States is 'the most scientifically advanced nation the world has ever known' precisely because it has been the most Bible-based society the world has ever known! And that includes belief in the biblical account of Creation, the Fall and the Flood.[26]

Again, CMI is not a lobby group, and it opposes legislation for *compulsion* of creation teaching (see page 29).[27] But there is nothing wrong with giving legal protection to teachers who want to present scientific arguments against the sacred cow of evolution. Yet *Scientific American* and the intelligentsia are mortified by the possibility:

> As this article goes to press, the Ohio Board of Education is debating whether to mandate such a change. Some antievolutionists, such as Philip E. Johnson, a law professor at the University of California

---

26. See Sarfati, J., "The biblical roots of modern science," 29 September 2009, creation.com/roots.

27. See also "The teaching of creation in public schools," creation.com/the-teaching-of-creation-in-schools.

at Berkeley and author of *Darwin on Trial,* admit that they intend for intelligent-design theory to serve as a 'wedge' for reopening science classrooms to discussions of God. [*SA* 78]

Horrors, discuss God in the classroom?  By this 'reasoning', John Rennie would have to blast Rufus Porter, a believer in biblical creation, who founded his own journal *Scientific American* for a similar purpose (see page 11)!

Rennie acknowledges the difficulty in answering creationists in the classroom, yet he slams their integrity:

> Besieged teachers and others may increasingly find themselves on the spot to defend evolution and refute creationism.  The arguments that creationists use are typically specious and based on misunderstandings of (or outright lies about) evolution, but the number and diversity of the objections can put even well-informed people at a disadvantage. [*SA* 78]

Is it possible that the 'well-informed' find the creationist arguments convincing because they recognize the validity of them? And most real scientists who *Scientific American* would call 'well-informed' actually have no use for evolution in their work!

Yet Rennie believes it is his duty to do his very best to shore up the cause of the embattled evolutionists with his cover story on 'creationist nonsense'.

> To help with answering them, the following list rebuts some of the most common 'scientific' arguments raised against evolution.  It also directs readers to further sources for information and explains why creation science has no place in the classroom. [*SA* 79]

By heaping together the best 'science' of evolutionists to 'rebut' creation, *Scientific American* has actually done us all a favor.  The remaining chapters of this book will show, in detail, how weak the 'best' arguments are, buttressing believers and challenging unbelievers to reconsider their assumptions about the validity of evolutionist propaganda.

# UNIT 2

## CLAIM 2:

# Evolution is Well Supported by the Evidence

*Evolutionists claim that they have found abundant, observable evidence of evolution.*

# Chapter 4

# Argument: Natural Selection Leads to Speciation

*Evolutionists say, 'Natural selection has been observed to cause profound changes in populations—providing abundant evidence for speciation.'*

## Galápagos finches—evolution in action?[1]

The opening episode of the PBS *Evolution* series makes much of the Galápagos finches—considered one of the classic evidences of 'evolution in action'. But PBS admits that Darwin didn't even realize that the birds were finches and he failed to label which island they came from. All the same, he managed to acquire this information, and he eventually concluded that they had descended from mainland finches with modification—just as the biblical Creation/Fall/Flood/Migration model would predict!

Darwin rightly postulated that all the varieties of finches, with varying beaks suited for their different food sources, were all descended from the same

---

1. See also Cosner, L. and Sarfati, J., "The Birds of the Galápagos," *Creation* **31**(3):28–31, 2009, creation.com/galapagos-birds.

sort of finch and the different varieties of finch arose over time.[2] And he argued reasonably that the ancestral island finches were descended from mainland ones.

But this is what biblical creationists would believe too, with a global Flood and subsequent migration from Ararat via continents to islands. So Darwin's arguments only work against a compromised creationist view, not the biblical view. (Present-day 'progressive creationists' hold essentially the same view as Darwin's opponents, so they are trying to fight a battle that was lost 150 years ago—but wouldn't have been if Christians had not compromised on the Earth's age and the global Flood.)

Here is a scenario: Suppose some finches with the genetic information for a wide variety of beaks came to the islands in a storm. And that some were on an island where the main food source was hard seeds. Birds with genes for thick and strong beaks could cope with them better, so would be better fed, and thus more likely to leave offspring. But birds on an island with few seeds but

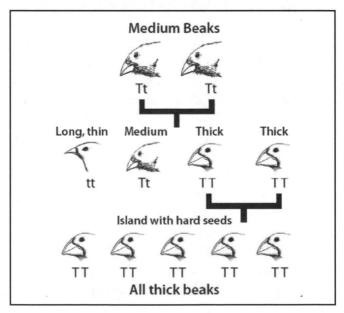

lots of grubs would do better with longer and thinner beaks, so they

2.    Cromie, W., "How Darwin's finches got their beaks," *Harvard Gazette*, news.harvard.edu/gazette/2006/08.24/31-finches.html, 24 August 2006.

could poke deeper into the ground and pull out their prey.

This is indeed an example of adaptation and natural selection. But note that it actually *removes* genes from the populations—on seed-rich islands with few grubs, information for long, slender beaks would likely be lost; while the information for thick, strong beaks would be lost on grub-rich (seed-poor) islands. So this change is in the *opposite direction* from goo-to-you evolution, which requires *new* genes with *new information.*[3] It can hardly be over-emphasized: *natural selection is not evolution;*[4] indeed, natural selection was discovered by creationists before Darwin[5] and is now an important part of the creation model.

The problem is that Darwin and the PBS series taught that this adaptation could explain the General Theory of Evolution. But the finch beak variation is merely the result of selection of *existing* genetic information, while the GTE requires *new* information. Also, an 18-year study by zoologist Peter Grant showed that a new species could arise in only 200 years,[6] which is inadvertent support for the biblical model of rapid speciation.[7] However, another problem with using these finches is that the variation seems to be cyclic—while a drought resulted in a slight increase in beak size, the change was reversed when the rains returned. So it looks more like *built-in* adaptability to various climatic conditions than anything to do with the GTE.

*Darwin's attempt to explain variations between finches underscores a fundamental point in the debate between evolution and creation: that facts do not speak for themselves, but are always interpreted within a framework.* Creationists don't deny a single observation an evolutionist makes, but find that they virtually

3.   Wieland, C., "The evolution train's a-comin' (Sorry, a-goin'—in the wrong direction)," *Creation* **24**(2):16–19, 2002, creation.com/train.

4.   Wieland, C., "Muddy Waters, Clarifying the confusion about natural selection," *Creation* **23**(3):26–29, 2001; creation.com/muddy.

5.   Grigg, R., "Darwin's illegitimate brainchild," *Creation* **26**(2):39–41, 2004; creation.com/brainchild.

6.   Grant, P.R., "Natural Selection and Darwin's Finches," *Scientific American* **265**(4):60–65, October 1991.

7.   See Wieland, C., "Darwin's Finches: Evidence supporting rapid post-Flood adaptation," *Creation* **14**(3):22–23, 1992, creation.com/darwins-finches.

always make better sense when interpreted within the biblical framework, as opposed to a compromised one. Therefore it shouldn't be surprising that many of the alleged 'evidences' for evolution actually turn out to support the biblical model.

PBS also discusses the change in beak length of hummingbirds, to adapt to changes in the lengths of flowers where they obtain nectar. But the same points apply—no evidence was produced that any new information is required for these changes, as opposed to selection of already-existing information.

## What is the biblical creationist model?

Perhaps the most frequently repeated mistake that evolutionists make in their attacks on creation is to assert that 'natural selection' and 'speciation' prove evolution and disprove the biblical account of origins. Their bait-and-switch[8] arguments imply that creationists believe in 'fixity of species'. The glossary for the PBS *Evolution* series' *Online Course for Teachers: Teaching Evolution* explicitly makes this empty allegation:

> In Creationism, species are described as "fixed" in the sense that they are believed not to change their form, or appearance, through time.

But no reputable creationist denies speciation—in fact, it is an important part of creationist biology. In fact, "fixity of species" was promoted by Darwin's anti-biblical mentor Lyell, and rejected by biblical creationists such as Athanasius Kircher before him (see page 76). In the previous chapter, I showed that the real issue is whether evolution can explain the *increase of genetic information content*—enough changes to turn microbes into men, *not* simple change through time. Before laying to rest the evolutionists' pointless arguments on this issue, it might be helpful to review the creationist model in detail.

---

8. See Sarfati, J., *The Greatest Hoax on Earth?* ch. 1, 2010; Walker, T., "Don't fall for the bait and switch: Sloppy language leads to sloppy thinking," *Creation* 29(4):38–39, 2007, creation.com/baitandswitch.

## Biblical 'kinds' are not modern species

Creationists, starting from the Bible, believe that God created different *kinds* of organisms, which reproduced 'after their kinds' (Gen. 1:11, 12, 21, 24, 25). Thus the biblical kinds would have *originally* been distinct biological species, i.e. a population of organisms that can interbreed to produce fertile offspring but that cannot so breed with a different biological species.

But creationists point out that the biblical 'kind' is larger than one of *today's* 'species'. Each of the original kinds was created with a vast amount of information. God made sure that the original creatures had enough variety in their genetic information so that their descendants could adapt to a wide variety of environments.

Based on the biblical criterion for kinds, creationists have made several deductions about the modern descendants of the original creations. They deduce, for example, that as long as two modern creatures can hybridize with true fertilization, the two creatures are descended from the same kind.[9] Also, if two creatures can hybridize with the same third creature, they are all members of the same kind.[10] The hybridization criterion is a valid *operational definition*, which could *in principle* enable researchers to list all the kinds. The implication is one-way—hybridization is evidence that two creatures *are* the same kind, but it does *not* necessarily follow that if hybridization *cannot* occur then they are *not* members of the same kind (failure to hybridize could be due to degenerative mutations). After all, there are couples who can't have children, and we don't classify them as a different species, let alone a different kind.

The boundaries of the kind do not always correspond to any given man-made classification such as species, genus, family, etc. But this is not the fault of the biblical term 'kind'; it is actually due to inconsistencies in the man-made classification system. That is, several organisms classified as different 'species', and even different genera or higher groupings, can produce fertile offspring.

9.  Marsh, F.L., *Variation and Fixity in Nature*, Pacific Press, Mountain View, CA, USA, p. 37, 1976.

10. Scherer, S., "Basic Types of Life," p. 197; ch. 8 of Dembski, W. A., *Mere Creation: Science, Faith and Intelligent Design*, Downers Grove, IL, 1998.

This means that they are really the same species that has several varieties, hence a *polytypic* (many type) species. A good example is Kekaimalu the wholphin, a fertile hybrid between male false killer whale (*Pseudorca crassidens*) and a female bottlenose dolphin (*Tursiops truncatus*), i.e. between two different so-called *genera*.[11] There are more examples in reference 9.

Biologists have identified several ways that a loss of genetic information through mutations (copying mistakes) can lead to new species—e.g. the loss of a  protein's ability to recognize 'imprinting' marks, 'jumping genes', natural selection, and genetic drift. When these mutations take place in small populations, they can sometimes result in sterile or nonviable offspring. Or changes in song or color might result in birds that no longer recognize a mate, so they no longer interbreed. Either way, a new 'species' is formed.[12] Thus each created kind may have been the ancestor of several present-day species.

But again, it's important to stress that speciation has nothing to do with *real* evolution (GTE), because it involves *sorting* and *loss* of genetic information, rather than *new* information.

## The biblical model predicts rapid speciation

The biblical Creation/Fall/Flood/Migration model would also predict *rapid* formation of new varieties and even species. This is because all the modern varieties of land vertebrates must have descended from comparatively few animals that disembarked from the Ark only around 4,500 years ago. In fact, scholars before Darwin predicted that there must be some means of variation for this reason, such as Athanasius Kircher (1602–1680) and Anglican Bishop John Wilkins (1614–1672), the founder of the metric system and the first secretary of the Royal Society.[13]

In contrast, Darwin thought that this process would

---

11. Batten, D., "Ligers and wholphins? What next?" *Creation* 22(3):28–33, June 2000, creation.com/liger.

12. For example, see Bell, P., "Genetic engineers unwind species barrier," *Creation* 25(4):52–53, 2003, creation.com/unwind.

13. See also Sarfati, J., *The Greatest Show on Earth?* Ch. 2, 2010.

normally take eons. It turns out that the very evidence claimed by evolutionists to support their theory supports the biblical model.

Biologists have identified several instances of rapid adaptation, including guppies on Trinidad, lizards in the Bahamas, daisies on the islands of British Columbia and house mice on Madeira.[14] Another good example is a new 'species' of mosquito that can't interbreed with the parent population, arising in the London Underground train system (the 'Tube') in only 100 years. The rapid change has 'astonished' evolutionists, but should delight creationists.[15] *Scientific American* admits as much.

> These days even most creationists acknowledge that microevolution has been upheld by tests in the laboratory (as in studies of cells, plants and fruit flies) and in the field (as in Grant's studies of evolving beak shapes among Galápagos finches). [*SA* 80]

And why should creationists deny such things? All of this so-called microevolution is part of a created and fallen world, but has never been observed to add new genetic information. In fact, the sorts of changes which are observed are the wrong type to drive the evolutionary story.[16] *Scientific American* is forced to make a pointless claim about evidence of 'profound' changes:

> Natural selection and other mechanisms—such as chromosomal changes, symbiosis and hybridization—can drive profound changes in populations over time. [*SA* 80]

Again, do these profound changes *increase information*? No—populations are seen *losing* information, and adapting within the constraints of the information they already have. In contrast, goo-to-you evolution requires something quite different—the

14. Catchpoole, D. and Wieland, C., "Speedy species surprise," *Creation* **23**(2):13–15, 2001, creation.com/speedy.

15. See Wieland, C., "Brisk Biters," *Creation* **21**(2):41, 1999, creation.com/brisk-biters.

16. See Wieland, C., "The evolution train's a-coming," *Creation* **24**(2), 2002, creation.com/train.

progressive addition of massive amounts of genetic information that is *novel* not only to that population, but to the entire biosphere.

## Straw man 1: Natural selection can't explain new species

*Scientific American* falls for the same straw man argument as PBS, failing to recognize that creationists accept new species arising within the kind. Creationists recognize how reproductive isolation can result from information loss. (See previous discussion.)

### 11. Natural selection might explain microevolution, but it cannot explain the origin of new species and higher orders of life.

> Evolutionary biologists have written extensively about how natural selection could produce new species. For instance, in the model called allopatry, developed by Ernst Mayr of Harvard University, if a population of organisms were isolated from the rest of its species by geographical boundaries, it might be subjected to different selective pressures. Changes would accumulate in the isolated population. If those changes became so significant that the splinter group could not or routinely would not breed with the original stock, then the splinter group would be *reproductively isolated* and on its way toward becoming a new species. [*SA* 82]

Indeed, creationists point out that Mayr's allopatric model would explain the origin of the different people groups ('races') after the confusion of languages at Babel induced small population groups to spread out all over the earth.[17] Of course, the modern people groups are *not* reproductively isolated and are still a single biological species.

Creationists also point out that the mountainous topography of the Ark's landing place would also be ideal for geographical

---

17. Wieland, C., *One Human Family: The Bible, Science Race and Culture*, Creation Book Publishers, 2011.

isolation. This would allow much post-Flood diversification from comparatively few (~8,000) kinds of land vertebrates, by splitting up the original high genetic variety.[18]

Note that the reproductive isolation is an informationally negative change, even if beneficial, because it blocks the interchange of genetic information between populations.

Evolutionists brag that natural selection is the best studied of the evolutionary mechanisms, but these studies show that it has nothing to do with evolution of more complex life forms! All we observe it doing is *removing* information, not adding it. *Scientific American* suggests that there are other feasible mechanisms to explain evolution, but they do not hold up, either.

> Natural selection is the best studied of the evolutionary mechanisms, but biologists are open to other possibilities as well. Biologists are constantly assessing the potential of unusual genetic mechanisms for causing speciation or for producing complex features in organisms. Lynn Margulis of the University of Massachusetts at Amherst and others have persuasively argued that some cellular organelles, such as the energy-generating mitochondria, evolved through the symbiotic merger of ancient organisms. [*SA* 82]

The *endosymbiosis* theory has many problems, such as the lack of evidence that prokaryotes are capable of ingesting another cell and keeping it alive, and the large differences in genes between mitochondria and prokaryotes.[19] *Scientific American* admits that it's open to any other mechanism to explain nature—*as long as it excludes God!*

> Thus, science welcomes the possibility of evolution resulting from forces beyond natural selection. Yet those forces must be natural; they cannot be attributed to the actions of mysterious creative intelligences

---

18. See Wieland, C., "Speciation conference brings good news for creationists," *JoC* 11(2):135–136, 1997, creation.com/speciation-conference.

19. See Batten, D., "Did cells acquire organelles such as mitochondria by gobbling up other cells?," creation.com/symbiont, 6 July 2000.

whose existence, in scientific terms, is unproved. [*SA* 82]

We have already cited (pp. 51 ff.) more honest admissions by evolutionists Lewontin and Todd about their a *priori* rejection of a designer before even examining the evidence. But evolutionary propaganda for public consumption persists in claiming that evolution is accepted purely on scientific grounds.

## Straw man 2: Evolutionists have seen species evolve

*Scientific American* tries to make hay with this straw man, devoting *two* points to 'proving' natural selection and speciation. Informed creationists don't teach against these biological processes—even though some 'day-age' advocates, like Hugh Ross,[20] do.

### 12. Nobody has ever seen a new species evolve.

> Speciation is probably fairly rare and in many cases might take centuries. [SA 82]

It might take centuries, but it *need* not. In fact, speciation can happen much faster than most evolutionists (and day-age advocates) realize. Creationists following the biblical Creation-Fall-Flood-Migration model expect such rapid *non-evolutive* speciation, as we pointed out on page 76.

> Furthermore, recognizing a new species during a formative stage can be difficult, because biologists sometimes disagree about how best to define a species. The most widely used definition, Mayr's Biological Species Concept, recognizes a species as a distinct community of reproductively isolated populations—sets of organisms that normally do not or cannot breed outside their community. In practice, this standard can be difficult to apply to organisms isolated by distance or terrain or to plants (and, of course, fossils do not breed). Biologists

---

20. See Sarfati, J., "Ten major differences between calendar-day and day-age creationists," creation.com/ross_yvo, 9 February 2001.

therefore usually use organisms' physical and behavioral traits as clues to their species membership. [*SA* 82]

We agree. It's important to note this difficulty in defining 'species' whenever evolutionists claim that creationists don't have a consistent definition of 'kinds' (which we do, as discussed before). We also agree with *Scientific American*'s recognition of recent experiments that have caused artificial speciation.

> Nevertheless, the scientific literature does contain reports of apparent speciation events in plants, insects and worms. In most of these experiments, researchers subjected organisms to various types of selection— for anatomical differences, mating behaviors, habitat preferences and other traits—and found that they had created populations of organisms that did not breed with outsiders. For example, William R. Rice of the University of New Mexico and George W. Salt of the University of California at Davis demonstrated that if they sorted a group of fruit flies by their preference for certain environments and bred those flies separately over 35 generations, the resulting flies would refuse to breed with those from a very different environment. [*SA* 82–83]

None of this is news to informed creationists. Once again, there is no new information, but sorting and loss of already existing information.

## Ecology proves evolution?

While evolutionists claim that natural selection is the best-studied mechanism for evolution, they also must explain the real-life processes behind natural selection. Their discussion of ecology is very interesting (and factual), but it tells us nothing about GTE.

## Changing populations within healthy forest ecosystems

For example, PBS 3 devotes a whole segment to show how a healthy forest ecosystem has a large carnivore at the top of the food chain, which can causes drastic changes in the population of the forest. It takes 100 pounds of plant to feed 10 pounds of herbivore, which in turn feeds 1 pound of carnivore. So the existence of carnivores indicates the health of the supporting animals and plants. Later on in the program, Wildlife Conservation Society biologist Alan Rabinowitz claims that this healthy forest exhibits "evolution going on around us," but all he means is the replacement of one species with another. Of course, *already-existing* species replacing other already-existing species has nothing to do with the origin of *new* species with new genetic *information*. Once again, 'evolution' is a vacuous catch-all term, with any change in population numbers tossed out to the unwary listener as evidence of the goo-to-you theory.

## Founder effect

Then the PBS program moves on to isolated habitats and the 'founder effect'. This is where a single breeding pair or pregnant female colonizes a new niche, and carries only a fraction of the gene pool. Therefore its descendants also contain a small fraction of the original gene pool, so the new population can be very different from the old. This also offers no comfort or support to the notion of evolution because the new population has less genetic information than the old.

## Invasion—the leafy spurge

Another ecological topic is biological invaders, the bane of all countries that depend on agriculture and livestock to feed their people and earn export dollars. The invaders are often more mobile and adaptive, so they out-compete native species. Modern technology has vastly increased the rate of hostile invasions, as animals stow away on ships and in the undercarriages of airplanes, although some species have been introduced deliberately. Fordham University paleoecologist David Burney investigated what happened in Hawaii when Polynesians and then Europeans introduced new species. He claimed:

> Evolution has now entered a new mode. Something

altogether new is happening, and it has to do with what humans do to the evolutionary process. [PBS 3]

Ho hum, this is just another example of replacement of one species with another, which again has nothing to do with showing how particles could have turned into people.

Pioneers introduced a weed called leafy spurge into North Dakota from Russia, and it 'threatens to kill off all native grasses.' A cattle rancher claimed on PBS that 'it is a cancer to the land ... it makes the land just totally useless.' Actually, the first claim is an exaggeration, and the second is a matter of perspective—sheep and goat farmers would have no problems.

But the rancher said that herbicides were very expensive, so the narrator asks:

> ... what's left?   ... The solution may be another invader—discovered when scientists learned what kept Leafy Spurge in check in its native Russia.  It's the flea beetle—a case of fighting evolutionary fire with fire. [PBS 3]

Canisters of flea beetles are dropped from airplanes, then the narrator says:

> So now we're in a race most of us don't even know we're running—to learn as much as possible about evolution before it's too late. [PBS 3]

Huh?  Using already-existing enemies of the leafy spurge requires 'evolution'?  This must be the nadir of the contentless nature of this word, even by the pathetic standards of the PBS series.   Farmers have used such common-sense biological controls for centuries, well before Darwin.  Interestingly, one of the classic cases of successful biological control was the defeat of Australia's cactus invader, the Prickly Pear, through the introduction of the *Cactoblastis* organism.   John Mann, the scientist responsible for saving Australia from ecological and economic ruin in this way, was heaped with accolades and honours for his feat.  Mann was a convinced biblical creationist, who was interviewed before his death by *Creation* magazine.[21]

## Symbiosis

PBS 3 also describes the leaf-cutting ants of Brazil. They form colonies containing eight million insects, and they cut leaves into pieces and bring them to the nest, but they don't eat them. Rather, other leafcutter ants mulch them and use the mulch to grow a fungus 'garden'. This fungus is used as food for the young leafcutters, which thus depend on the fungus for survival, but the fungus depends on the ants to provide the mulch.

But this fungus garden has a 'weed', a virulent mould that badly hinders the fungal growth. To combat this, some ants have a white waxy coating that is now known to be tangled mats of bacteria that produce antibiotics that kill the mould.

Presumably, by this stage in the series, the producers hope that viewers are so indoctrinated in evolution that they don't even need to try to produce evidence. To the diehard evolutionist, any phenomenon at all can be adduced as 'evidence' for evolution. In this case, they don't bother to explain how such a complex symbiosis could have evolved, but merely assert that the bacteria and mould are products of an arms race lasting 50 million years.

## Predator–prey, driving force of evolution?

While evolutionists discuss natural selection and speciation, they like to emphasize the bloodshed and violence that drives these biological changes. They see 'Nature, red in tooth and claw', in the memorable phrase from the very long 1850 poem *In Memoriam, A.H.H.* by Alfred Lord Tennyson (1809–1892). In debates they love to pull out this as 'knock-down' evidence against Christians, believing it disproves the possibility of a benevolent, wise Creator—following Darwin (see page 34). The fact that Tennyson's poem predated Darwin's *Origin* shows that Darwin was greatly influenced by philosophical ideas of his day.

But their viewpoint overlooks an obvious incident in biblical history—Adam's sin and God's subsequent curse on the whole

21. "Interview with creationist biological control expert, Dr John Mann, M.B.E.," *Creation* 5(2):20–21, 1982, creation.com/mann.

creation, as I will explain further on page 88. Unfortunately, many in the 'Intelligent Design Movement' refuse to invoke the Bible which provides the *only* plausible answer, so they are stumped by this argument.[22] So, upon closer inspection, the predator–prey paradigm testifies to the accuracy of the biblical account and offers nothing to resolve the fundamental flaw of the General Theory of Evolution: where does new genetic information come from?

Episode 4 of the PBS *Evolution* series aims to show that these violent biological forces, rather than the environmental ones, drive evolution most strongly, based largely on extensive interviews with the atheistic sociobiologist Edward O. Wilson. The title of PBS 4, 'The Evolutionary Arms Race!' reflects the struggle between predator and prey: as a prey evolves stronger defense mechanisms, an attacker must evolve stronger mechanisms to survive, and vice versa. Of course, evolutionary biologists think there is no design behind this: the only prey that survive have *chance* copying mistakes in their genes that confer a strong defense, and they pass on these genes to their offspring. Faced with these stronger defense mechanisms, only those predators that *happen* to have mutations conferring better attacking power will be able to eat the prey, while the others starve and fail to pass on their genes.

But as explained on pages 53 ff., real evolution requires changes that *increase genetic information*, while non-information-increasing changes are part of the creation model. None of the examples presented in episode 4 prove that information has increased, so they provide no support for evolution or against creation.

## Poison newt

PBS takes viewers to Oregon, where there were mysterious deaths of campers, but it turned out that newts were found boiled in the coffee pot. These Rough-skinned Newts (*Taricha granulosa*) secrete a deadly toxin from their skin glands so powerful that even a pinhead-sized amount can kill an adult human. They are the deadliest salamanders on Earth. So scientists investigated why

---

22. This is why my later book, *By Design* (2008), has chapters on 'bad design' and creatures designed to hurt other creatures, which overtly invoke the biblical history of the Fall and the Flood.

this newt should have such a deadly toxin.

They theorized that a predator was driving this 'evolution', and they found that the Common Garter Snake (*Thamnophis sirtalis*) was the newt's only predator. Most snakes will be killed by the newt's toxin, but the Common Garter Snake just loses muscle control for a few hours, which could of course have serious consequences. But the newts were also driving the 'evolution' of the snakes—they also had various degrees of resistance to the newt toxin.

Are these conclusions correct? Yes, it is probably correct that the predators and prey are driving each other's changes, and that they are the result of mutations and natural selection. Although it might surprise the ill-informed anti-creationist that creationists accept mutations and selection, it shouldn't be so surprising to anyone who understands the biblical Creation/Fall model (see pages 76 ff).

So is this proof of particles-to-people evolution? Not at all. There is no proof that the changes increase genetic information. In fact, the reverse seems to be true.

The snakes with greater resistance have a cost—they move more slowly. Since PBS provided no explanation of the poison's activity, it's fair to propose possible scenarios to explain the phenomenon under a biblical framework (it would be hypocritical for evolutionists to object, since they often produce hypothetical 'just-so' stories to explain what they cannot see):

> Suppose the newt's poison normally reacts with a particular neurotransmitter in its victims to produce something that halts all nerve impulses, resulting in death. But if the snake had a mutation which *reduced* the production of this neurotransmitter, then the newt's poison would have fewer targets to act upon. Another possibility is a mutation in the snake altering the neurotransmitter's precise structure so that its shape no longer matches the protein. Either way, the poison would be less effective. But at the same time, either mutation would slow nerve impulses, making the snake's muscle movement slower.

So this is an information *loss* in the snake that happens to confer an advantage. This is far from the only example. The best known is sickle-cell anemia, a common blood disorder in which a mutation causes the sufferer's hemoglobin to form the wrong shape and fail to carry oxygen. People who carry two copies of the sickle-cell gene (homozygous) often develop fatal anemia. But this misshapen hemoglobin also resists the malaria parasite (*Plasmodium*). So humans who are heterozygous (have both a normal and abnormal gene) have some advantage in areas where malaria is prevalent, even though half their hemoglobin is less effective at its job of carrying oxygen.[23] Another example is wingless beetles, which survive on windy islands because they won't fly and be blown into the sea.[24]

As for the newt, likewise, increased secretion of poison can result without any new information. One possibility is an information-*losing* mutation that disables a gene controlling the production of the poison. Then it would be over-produced, which would be an advantage in defending against the snake, but a wasteful use of resources otherwise.

There are other related examples, e.g., one way that the *Staphylococcus* bacterium becomes resistant to penicillin is *via* a mutation that disables a control gene for production of penicillinase, an enzyme that destroys penicillin. When it has this mutation, the bacterium *over*-produces this enzyme, which means it is resistant to huge amounts of penicillin. But in the wild, this mutant bacterium is less fit, because it squanders resources by producing unnecessary penicillinase.[25,26]

Another example is a cattle breed called the *Belgian Blue*. This is very valuable to beef farmers because it has 20–30% more muscle than average cattle, and its meat is lower in fat. Normally, muscle

23. Konotey-Ahulu, F., "Sickle-cell anemia does not prove evolution!" *Creation* **16**(2):40–41, 1994, creation.com/sickle. See also interview in *Creation* **29**(1):16–19, 2006.

24. See Wieland, C., "Beetle bloopers: even a defect can be an advantage sometimes," *Creation* **19**(3):30, 1997, creation.com/beetle.

25. See Wieland, C., "Superbugs not super after all," *Creation* **20**(1):10–13, 1998, creation.com/superbugs.

26. Sarfati, J., "Anthrax and antibiotics: Is evolution relevant?" creation.com/anthrax, 8 April 2005.

growth is regulated by a number of proteins, such as *myostatin.* However, Belgian Blues have a mutation that *deactivates* the myostatin gene, so the muscles grow uncontrolled and become very large. This mutation has a cost, in reduced fertility.[27] These cattle also suffer from decreased fat and bone mass, making them more susceptible to stress fractures.[28] A different mutation of the same gene is also responsible for the very muscular Piedmontese cattle. Genetic engineers have bred muscular mice by the same principle, and the same mutation has been observed in a German child dubbed the 'superbaby'.[29]

In all these cases, a mutation causes information *loss,* even though it might be considered 'beneficial'. Therefore it is in the *opposite* direction required for particles-to-people evolution, which requires the generation of *new* information.

## Did God create carnivory?

According to the Bible, the original diet of both humans and animals was vegetarian (Genesis 1:29–30). So how do creationists explain carnivory today? Episode 4 of the PBS *Evolution* series showed many examples of animals killing other animals, which doesn't seem like a 'very good' creation (Gen. 1:31). According to the Bible, death was introduced with Adam's sin (Genesis 2:17, Gen. 3:17–19, Rom. 5:12, 1 Cor. 15:21–22). While these verses refer explicitly to human death, Genesis 3 is clear that Adam's sin had further unpleasant effects because Adam was the federal head of creation. The Reformer John Calvin commented on Genesis 3:19:

> 'Therefore, we may know, that whatever unwholesome things may be produced, are not natural fruits of the earth, but are corruptions which originate from sin.'[30]

27. Travis, J., Muscle-bound cattle reveal meaty mutation, *Science News* **152**(21):325, 22 November 1997.

28. Lightner, J., "Mutations, selection, and the quest for meatier livestock," *JoC* **19**(2):18–20, 2005; creation.com/meatier.

29. Sarfati, J., "The superbaby mutation," *Creation* **27**(1):13, 2004; creation.com/superbaby.

30. Calvin, J., *Genesis,* 1554; Banner of Truth, Edinburgh, UK, 1984, p. 180.

This is supported by Paul's teaching of Romans 8:20–22, that God subjected the whole creation to futility, and many commentators believe Paul was alluding to Genesis 3. Further support comes from the fact that the restored creation will have no carnivory (Isaiah 65:25).[31]

The Bible doesn't specifically explain how carnivory originated, but since creation was finished after Day 6 (Gen. 2:1–3), there is no possibility that God created new carnivorous animals. Instead, creationists have three explanations in general, although the specific explanation depends on the particular case.[32]

1. The Bible appears not to regard insects as living in the same sense as humans and vertebrate animals—the Hebrew never refers to them as *nephesh chayyāh* (Hebrew, meaning living souls/creatures), unlike humans and even fish (Gen. 1:20, 2:7).

2. Before the Fall, many attack/defense structures could have been used in a vegetarian lifestyle. For example, even today, some baby spiders use their webs to trap pollen for food,[33] and the *Bagheera kiplingi* spider is predominately vegetarian.[34] There have also been several documented cases of lions and cats that thrived on meatless diets.[35] Even many poisons actually have beneficial purposes in small amounts.[36] Even PBS pointed out that microbes 'help prime the immune system' and that many allergies

31. Smith, H.B., "Cosmic and universal death from Adam's Fall: an exegesis of Romans 8:19–23a," *JoC* **21**(1):75–85, 2007; creation.com/romans8.

32. This topic is covered more fully in chapter 6 of Batten, D., ed., *et al.*, *The Creation Answers Book*, 3 ed., Creation Book Publishers, 2009.

33. "Pollen-eating spiders," *Creation* **22**(3):8, 2000, creation.com/spiders_pollen; *Nature Australia*, Summer 1999–2000, p. 5.

34. Catchpoole, D., "Vegetarian spider," *Creation* **31**(4):46, 2009.

35. Catchpoole, D., "The lion that wouldn't eat meat," *Creation* **22**(2):22–23, 2000, creation.com/lion; Catchpoole, D., "Lea, the spaghetti lioness," *Creation* **29**(4):44–45, 2007, creation.com/spag; Wieland, C. "The cat who refuses to eat meat," 28 April 2009, creation.com/vegcat.

36. See Bergman, J., "Understanding Poisons from a Creationist Perspective," *JoC* **11**(3):353–360, 1997, creation.com/poison.

might be due to a society that's too clean.

3. God foreknew the Fall, so He programmed creatures with the information for design features for attack and defense that they would need in a cursed world. This information was 'switched on' at the Fall.

For the poisonous newt, it seems that #3 is the best explanation for the molecular structure of the deadly toxin itself and the poison glands on the skin. In general, I believe #3 is the best explanation for structures that seem specifically designed for attack and defense.

## Evolution of pathogens

If evolutionists hope to find evidence of modern-day evolution, they have a perfect opportunity with pathogens. In just a few months, bacteria can go through hundreds of thousands of generations, equivalent to 'millions of years' in vertebrates. Yet despite this rapid change, the bacteria that we see today are essentially the same as the bacteria retrieved from the tombs of the pharaohs, and even with those discovered in salt crystals 'dated' millions of years old.[37]

## HIV resistance to drugs

PBS 1 claims that Darwin didn't really see evolution in action, but now we do. Supposedly the HIV, the cause of the modern AIDS epidemic, evolves resistance to drugs faster than we can make them. Because the virus can produce billions of copies per day, it can 'evolve' in minutes to hours. One researcher said that this rapid change would be a 'surprise' if we didn't have the concept of evolution. PBS also attempted to tug heartstrings, by portraying AIDS patients as 'victims of evolution.'

First, we see the equivocation—HIV producing HIV is supposed to show that particles could turn into people; but they're still HIV—they haven't changed into something else. Second, in

---

37. Batten, D., "Bugs in Brine," *Creation* **24**(4):10–13, 2002, creation.com/bugs-in-brine.

PBS 4, it's made clear that the related phenomenon of antibiotic resistance in bacteria took the medical community by surprise—this means that it wasn't a prediction of evolution, except after the fact. Third, they fail to demonstrate that new information is involved, and in fact the next segment of the program showed that the opposite is true:

Veronica Miller of the Goethe University in Germany experimented by ceasing all antiviral drug treatments to a patient. Without the drugs, the few surviving original ('wild') types that had infected the patient could grow more easily. It turned out that they easily out-competed the vast numbers of resistant forms that had developed in the hospital. She said this was a risk because the wild types were also more dangerous—more efficient than the new strains that had survived the earlier drug treatments. The superior efficiency and reproductive success of the wild type implies that the other 'evolved' strains acquired resistance due to a *loss* of information somewhere.

This should not be surprising, because the same is true of many examples of antibiotic resistance in bacteria. For example, some bacteria have an enzyme that usually has a useful purpose, but it also turns an antibiotic into a poison. That is, it's not the antibiotic *per se* that's damaging, but its chemical by-product from the bacterium's metabolism. So a mutation *disabling* this enzyme would render the antibiotic harmless. But this bacterium is still disabled, because the enzyme is now hindered, so the bacterium would be unable to compete in the wild with non-resistant ones. The information loss in both HIV and the bacterium is the *opposite* of what evolution requires.[38]

## Tuberculosis and antibiotic resistance

PBS describes microbes as a 'predator' of humans, although 'parasite' would be more accurate. Mummies show that the

---

38. See Wieland, C., "Has AIDS evolved?" *Creation* 12(3):29–32, 1990, creation.com/has-aids-evolved; Batten, D., "An information-gaining mutation in HIV?," 9 February 2008, creation.com/hiv; Sarfati, J., "Anthrax and antibiotics: Is evolution relevant?," 8 April 2005, creation.com/anthrax.

tubercle bacillus (TB), *Mycobacterium tuberculosis*, affected Egyptians 4000 years ago. The Black Death wiped out one-third of Europe's population in 1347–1351, and the Influenza pandemic of 1918–1919 killed 20 million people—more than World War 1 that had just ended.

After the world wars, antibiotics were considered the 'magic bullet', and there were optimistic claims even as late as 1969 that 'infectious diseases were a thing of the past'. But they failed to anticipate the development of resistance. This shows that bacterial resistance was hardly a 'prediction' of evolution, but is really a phenomenon they try to explain 'after the fact' as due to evolution. As will be shown, there is nothing to support molecules-to-man evolution; rather, a properly understood creation model makes good sense of the evidence.[39]

PBS 4 discussed a new strain of TB that had arisen in the overcrowded Russian prison system, containing malnourished prisoners with weakened immune systems. One inmate, 'Sasha' (a diminutive form of Alexandr), had failed to complete his course of antibiotics. This meant that a few bacteria survived because they had some resistance to the antibiotic, and then proliferated once the treatment stopped. But the program itself makes it clear that the resistance was already present, so this is *not* evolution, although it *is* natural selection.

These resistant bacteria are not confined to the prison, but have spread because of travel. One 19-year-old Russian student, 'Anna', has a strain resistant to five antibiotics. Immunologists predict that TB could soon claim 2–3 million lives per year.

But as shown, there is no proof that any antibiotic resistance is due to increased genetic information. The above example shows that the information was *already present*, and I previously explained how a *loss* of information could confer resistance. Sometimes bacteria can pass genes to each other by exchanging plasmids, and sometimes these genes confer resistance. But of course, these examples involve no new information produced in the biosphere.

---

39. See Mitchell, R. "Evolution and medicine," 22 November 2005, creation.com/evolution-and-medicine.

## Evolution of less harmful bacteria?

Paul Ewald of Amherst College claimed on PBS 4 that 'evolution' may not only be a problem, but could also be harnessed to 'evolve' less harmful bacteria. If a pathogen spreads by close contact between people, then it's in its best interest not to make people so sick that they can't move around. But those pathogens spread by water and insects tend to be deadly.

In the 1991 cholera epidemic in South America, a million people were infected, and 10,000 died. The bacterium (*Vibrio cholerae*) was spread by contaminated water, so 'evolved' high levels of toxicity. The solution was to clean the water supply, so that only healthier people could spread the germ. So the germ 'evolved' mildness, and many infected people didn't even develop symptoms.

But here again, there is indeed natural selection, but the result is that *Vibrio cholerae* turn into *Vibrio cholerae!* There is no proof that any new information was produced, but rather, selection of existing genetic variation.

### *Dog breeding and artificial selection*

PBS 4 compared the above changes in the cholera germ to breeding domestic dogs from wolves, but again this involved *loss* of information. Here's how:[40]

---

40. From Cosner, L., "Parade of mutants," *Creation* **32**(3):28–32, 2010, creation.com/pedigree.

In the example on the above (simplified for illustration), a single gene pair is shown under each dog as coming in two possible forms. One form of the gene (S) carries instructions for large size, the other (s) for small size.

In row 1, we start with medium-sized animals (Ss) interbreeding. Each of the offspring of these dogs can get one of either gene from each parent to make up their two genes.

In row 2, we see that the resultant offspring can have either large (SS), medium (Ss) or small (ss) size. But let's suppose that breeders want large dogs. They would select the largest dogs in the next generation to breed. Thus only the big dogs pass on genes to the next generation (line 3). So from then on, all the dogs will be a new, large variety. This is artificial selection, but natural selection would work on the same principle, if large dogs would do better in their environment. Note that:

1. They are now **adapted** to their environment, in this case breeders who want big dogs.

2. They are now more **specialized** than their ancestors on row 1.

3. This has occurred through **artificial selection**, and could have occurred through natural selection.

4. There have been **no new genes** added

5. In fact, genes have been lost from the population—i.e. there has been **a loss of genetic information**, the opposite of what microbe-to-man evolution needs in order to be credible.

6. Not only genes for smallness were lost, but any other genes these small dogs carried. They may have had genes for endurance, strong sense of smell, and other things, but they are lost from the population. Genes on their own are not selected; it's the *whole creature* and *all* the genes they carried.

Now the population is less able to adapt to future environmental changes—if small dogs became fashionable, or would perform better in some environment, they could not be bred from this population. They are also genetically impoverished since they lack the good genes that happened to be carried by the small dogs.

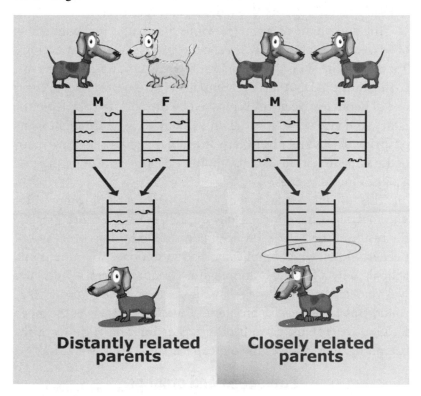

**Distantly related parents**

**Closely related parents**

## The dangers of inbreeding

The sort of artificial selection that has produced purebred dogs is deleterious for another reason: the expression of harmful mutations—genetic copying mistakes. Since the Fall, all creatures have accumulated large number of mutations. These mutations are accumulating much faster than previously thought[41]—at least 100 nucleotide substitutions (single-letter 'typos') per person per

41. Sanford, J.C., *Genetic Entropy and the Mystery of the Genome*, Ivan Press, 2005; see review of the book and the interview with the author in *Creation* **30**(4):45–47, 2008.

generation, according to geneticist Kondrashov[42]—and the rate might be as high as 300.[43] And this doesn't include even larger changes such as deletions, insertions, duplications, translocations, inversions and micro-satellite mutations. Evolutionist Kondrashov himself asked, "Why aren't we dead 100 times over?"[44]

The dogs in the diagram (previous page) inherited one stretch of DNA from each parent. We see the good genes and mutations. The dog on the left is the offspring of two distantly related parents, so the mother's DNA has different defects from the father's. Every one of her defective genes is masked by the backup copy from the father, and vice versa. But the unfortunate dog on the right is the offspring of close relatives; here, the father and mother have many of the same mutations. So in a number of spots, the dog inherited a pair of mutant genes.

This might explain why God prohibited brother-sister intermarriages from Moses' day on. But note that mutations are the result of the Fall—God originally created things "very good" (Genesis 1:31), which implies no bad mutations. So humans and animals only a few generations after Creation Week would have had very few mutations, which means that close intermarriage would not have been a problem. Therefore there was no need for God to prohibit close brother-sister intermarriage from the beginning, which solves the old canard, "Who was Mrs Cain?"[45]

## Pathogens and creation

Some people wonder where disease germs fit into the biblical framework, if God created everything 'very good'. Under this framework, obviously the Fall was responsible for disease, but how, if God had finished creating at the end of Creation Week?

---

42. Kondrashov, A.S., "Direct estimation of human nucleotide mutation rates at 20 loci causing Mendelian diseases," *Human Mutation* **21**:12–27, 2002.

43. Kondrashov, personal communication to Sanford, cited in *Genetic Entropy*, Ref. 67.

44. Kondrashov, A.S., "Contamination of the genome by very slightly deleterious mutations: why have we not died 100 times over?" *J. Theoret. Biol.* **175**:583–594, 1995.

45. See the *Creation Answers Book*, ch. 8, for more information.

The phenomenon described in the previous section can provide some insights. It clearly shows that even something usually known as a deadly germ can have a mild variant that causes no illness. Presumably something like this was created during Creation Week—even today, *Vibrio cholerae* has a role in the ecosystems of brackish waters and estuaries, and the original may have had a role living symbiotically with some people. Even its toxin probably has a beneficial function in small amounts, like most poisons. The virulence arose after the Fall, by natural selection of varieties producing more and more toxin as contaminated water became more plentiful. No new information would be needed for this process. Recent evidence shows that the *loss* of *chemotaxis*—the ability to move in response to changes in chemical concentrations—will markedly increase infectivity in an infant mouse model of cholera.[46]

Another likely example of virulence arising by information loss is the mycoplasmas, the smallest known self-reproducing organisms (parasitic bacteria with no cell walls and fewer than 1000 genes, found in the respiratory system and urogenital tracts of humans). Loss of genetic information, e.g. for amino acid synthesis, could have resulted in the mycoplasmas' becoming increasingly dependent on their hosts for survival.[47,48] Some clues to possible benign pre-Fall roles for viruses can be gleaned from functions they have even today. Viruses are non-living entities, which function like seeds and spores, transporting genes among plants and animals. They also help keep soil fertile, keep water clean and regulate gases in the atmosphere.[49] So once again, some alleged evidence for evolution actually provides support for the Creation/Fall model.

46. Merrell, D.S. *et al.*, "Host-induced epidemic spread of the cholera bacterium," *Nature* **417**(6889):642–644, 6 June 2002.

47. Wood, T.C., "Genome decay in the Mycoplasmas," *Impact* **340**, October 2001.

48. See Wieland, C., "Diseases on the Ark (Answering the Critics)," *JoC* **8**(1):16–18, 1994, creation.com/diseases.

49. Bergman, J., "Did God make pathogenic viruses?," *JoC* **13**(1):115–125, 1999, creation.com/viruses.

## *Has immunity evolved?*

In PBS 4, Stephen O'Brien of the National Cancer Institute wondered why the big cats have 'evolved' resistance to a disease deadly to humans. There is a Feline Immunodeficiency Virus (FIV) that should cause AIDS-like symptoms. Supposedly the cats' ancestors were almost wiped out by the virus, but some had resistant genes. Supposedly the FIV evolved to mildness.

The alleged evolution of HIV was dealt with on pages 90 ff. More interesting was the claim that about 10% of humans have a 'whopping mutation' that confers resistance to HIV. This turns out to be the *loss* of certain receptors on the immune cells preventing the HIV from docking on them. Again, this change is in the *opposite direction* required to change particles into people.

From mycoplasmas to big cats, from TB to poison newts, there's not a shred of evidence that might explain the evolution of new genetic information, but the *loss* that we see fits nicely with the biblical creationist model.

# Chapter 5

# Argument: Some Mutations are Beneficial

*Evolutionists say, 'Mutations and other biological mechanisms have been observed to produce new features in organisms.'*

W hen they begin to talk about mutations, evolutionists tacitly acknowledge that natural selection, by itself, cannot explain the rise of new genetic information. Somehow they have to explain the introduction of completely new genetic instructions for feathers and other wonders that never existed in 'simpler' life forms. So they place their faith in mutations.

In the process of defending mutations as a mechanism for creating new genetic code, they attack a straw man version of the creationist model, and they have *no* answer for the creationists' real scientific objections. *Scientific American* states their common straw man position and answer to it:

> **10. Mutations are essential to evolution theory, but mutations can only eliminate traits. They cannot produce new features.**
>
> On the contrary, biology has catalogued many traits produced by point mutations (changes at precise positions in an organism's DNA)—bacterial resistance to antibiotics, for example. [*SA* 82]

This is a serious misstatement of the creationist argument. The issue is not new *traits*, but new genetic information. In no known case is antibiotic resistance the result of new information. There are several ways that an information *loss* can confer resistance, as shown on pages 85 ff. On pages 72 and 93 ff., we have pointed out in various ways how new traits, even helpful, adaptive traits, can arise through *loss* of genetic information (which is to be expected from mutations).

> Mutations that arise in the homeobox (*Hox*) family of development-regulating genes in animals can also have complex effects. *Hox* genes direct where legs, wings, antennae and body segments should grow. In fruit flies, for instance, the mutation called *Antennapedia* causes legs to sprout where antennae should grow. [*SA* 82]

Once again, there is no new information! Rather, a mutation in the hox gene results in already-existing information being switched on in the wrong place.[1] The hox gene merely moved legs to the wrong place; it did not produce any of the information that actually constructs the legs, which in ants and bees include a wondrously complex mechanical and hydraulic structure that enables these insects to stick to surfaces.[2]

> These abnormal limbs are not functional, but their existence demonstrates that genetic mistakes can produce complex structures, which natural selection can then test for possible uses. [*SA* 82]

Amazing—natural selection can 'test for possible uses' of 'non-functional' (i.e. *useless*!) limbs in the wrong place. Such deformities would be active hindrances to survival.

### Gene switches: means of Evolution?

William Bateson (1861–1926), who added the word 'genetics'

---

1. See Batten, D., "Hox (homeobox) Genes — Evolution's Saviour?" creation.com/hox; DeWitt, D., Hox Hype — Has Macro-evolution Been Proven? creation.com/hox-hype.

2. See Sarfati, J., "Startling stickiness," *Creation* **24**(2):37, 2002; creation.com/stickiness.

to our vocabulary in 1909, found that embryos sometimes grew body parts in the wrong place. From this he theorized that there are underlying controls of certain body parts, and other controls governing where they go.

Ed Lewis investigated and won a Nobel Prize in 1995 for discovering a small set of genes that affect different body parts (*Hox* or *Homeobox*). They act like 'architects of the body'. Mutations in these can cause 'dramatic' changes. Many experiments have been performed on fruit flies (*Drosophila*), where poisons and radiation induced mutations.

The problem is that they are always harmful. One famous case is *Antennapedia*, where legs grow where antennae should be. PBS 2 showed an extra pair of wings on a fly, but failed to mention that they were a *hindrance* to flying because there are no accompanying muscles. Both these flies would be *eliminated* by natural selection.

Walter Gehring of the University of Basel (Switzerland) replaced a gene needed for eye development in a fruit fly with the corresponding gene from a mouse. The fly still developed normal fly eyes, i.e. compound eyes rather than lens/camera. This gene in both insects and mammals is called *Eyeless* because absence of this gene means no eyes will form.

However, there is obviously more to the differences between different animals. Eyeless is a *switch*—it turns on the genetic information needed for eyes. But evolution requires some way of generating the new information that's to be switched on. The information needed to build a compound eye is vastly different from that needed to build a lens/camera type of eye. By analogy, the *same* switch on an electric outlet/power socket can turn on a light or a laptop, but this hardly proves that a light evolved into a laptop!

All the same, the program says that *Eyeless* is one of a small number of common genes used in the embryonic development of many animals. The program illustrated this with diagrams. Supposedly all evolution needed to do was reshuffle packets of information into different combinations.

But as shown, known mutations in these genes cause monstrosities, and different switches are very distinct from what is switched on or off. Also, the embryo develops into its basic body plan *before* these genes start switching—obviously they can't be the cause of the plan before they are activated! But the common genes make perfect sense given the existence of a *single* Creator.[3]

## Increased amounts of DNA don't mean increased function

Biologists have discovered a whole range of mechanisms that can cause radical changes in the amount of DNA possessed by an organism. Gene duplication, polyploidy, insertions, etc., do not help explain evolution, however. They represent an increase in *amount* of DNA, but not an increase in the amount of functional genetic *information*—these mechanisms create nothing new. Macroevolution needs *new* genes (for making feathers on reptiles, for example), yet *Scientific American* completely misses this simple distinction:

> Moreover, molecular biology has discovered mechanisms for genetic change that go beyond point mutations, and these expand the ways in which new traits can appear. Functional modules within genes can be spliced together in novel ways. Whole genes can be accidentally duplicated in an organism's DNA, and the duplicates are free to mutate into genes for new, complex features. [*SA* 82]

In plants, but not in animals (possibly with rare exceptions), the doubling of all the chromosomes may result in an individual which can no longer interbreed with the parent type—this is called *polyploidy*. Although this may technically be called a new species, because of the breeding isolation, no new information has been produced, just repetitious doubling of *existing* information. If a malfunction in a printing press caused a book to be printed with every page doubled, it would not be more informative than the proper book. (Brave students of evolutionary professors might

---

3.  See also Batten, D., "A cat with four ears (not nine lives)," *Creation* **26**(4):56, 2004, creation.com/catears.

like to ask whether they would get extra marks for handing in two copies of the same assignment.)

Duplication of a single chromosome is normally harmful, as in Down's Syndrome. Insertions are a very efficient way of completely destroying the functionality of existing genes. Biophysicist Dr Lee Spetner in his book *Not By Chance* analyses examples of mutational changes that evolutionists have claimed to have been increases in information, and shows that they are actually examples of *loss of specificity*, which means they involved loss of information (which is to be expected from information theory).

The evolutionist's 'gene duplication idea' is that an existing gene may be doubled, and one copy does its normal work while the other copy is redundant and non-expressed. Therefore it is free to mutate free of selection pressure (to get rid of it). However, such 'neutral' mutations are powerless to produce new genuine information. Dawkins *et al.* point out that natural selection is the only possible naturalistic explanation for the immense design in nature (not a good one, as Spetner *et al.* have shown). Dawkins and others propose that random changes produce a new function, then this redundant gene becomes expressed somehow and is fine-tuned under the natural selective process.

This 'idea' is just a lot of hand-waving. It relies on a chance copying event, genes somehow being switched off, randomly mutating to something approximating a new function, then being switched on again so natural selection can tune it.

Furthermore, mutations do not occur in just the duplicated gene; they occur throughout the genome. Consequently, all the deleterious mutations in the rest of the genome have to be eliminated by the death of the unfit. Selective mutations in the target duplicate gene are extremely rare—it might represent only 1 part in 30,000 of the genome of an animal. The larger the genome, the bigger the problem, because the larger the genome, the lower the mutation rate that the creature can sustain without error catastrophe; as a result, it takes even longer for *any* mutation to occur, let alone a desirable one, in the duplicated gene. There just has not been enough time for such a naturalistic process to account for the amount of genetic information that we see in living things.

Dawkins and others have recognised that the 'information space' possible within just one gene is so huge that random changes without some guiding force could never come up with a new function. There could never be enough 'experiments' (mutating generations of organisms) to find anything useful by such a process. Note that an average gene of 1,000 base pairs represents $4^{1000}$ possibilities—that is $10^{602}$ (compare this with the number of atoms in the universe estimated at 'only' $10^{80}$). If every atom in the universe represented an 'experiment' every millisecond for the supposed 15 billion years of the universe, this could only try a maximum $10^{100}$ of the possibilities for the gene. So such a 'neutral' process cannot possibly find any sequence with specificity (usefulness), even allowing for the fact that more than just one sequence may be functional to some extent.

So Dawkins and company have the same problem as the advocates of neutral selection theory. Increasing knowledge of the molecular basis of biological functions has exploded the known 'information space' so that mutations and natural selection— with or without gene duplication, or any other known natural process—cannot account for the irreducibly complex nature of living systems.

## Hemoglobin: the result of gene duplication?

Yet *Scientific American* has the impertinence to claim that:

> Comparisons of the DNA from a wide variety of organisms indicate that this [duplication of genes] is how the globin family of blood proteins evolved over millions of years. [*SA* 82]

This is about the vital red blood pigment *hemoglobin* that carries the oxygen. It has four polypeptide chains and iron. Evolutionists believe that this evolved from an oxygen-carrying iron-containing protein found in muscles called *myoglobin*, which has only one polypeptide chain. However, there is no *demonstration* that gene duplication plus natural selection turned the one-chained myoglobin into the four-chained hemoglobin. Nor is there any adequate explanation of how the hypothetical intermediates would have had selective advantages.[4,5,6]

In fact, the proposed evolution of hemoglobin is far more complicated than *Scientific American* implies, though it requires a little advanced biology to understand. The α- and β-globin chains are encoded on genes on different chromosomes, so they are expressed independently. This expression must be controlled precisely, otherwise various types of anemia called *thalassemia* results. Also, there is an essential protein called AHSP (Alpha Hemoglobin Stabilizing Protein) which, as the name implies, stabilizes the α-chains, and also brings it to the β-chains. Otherwise the α-chains would precipitate and damage the red blood cells.

AHSP is one of many examples of a class of protein called *chaperones* which govern the folding of other proteins.[7] This is yet another problem for chemical evolutionary theories—how did the first proteins fold correctly without chaperones; and since the chaperones themselves are complex proteins, how did *they* fold?[8]

Identifying information-increasing mutations may be a small part of the whole evolutionary discussion, but it is a critical 'weak link' in the logical chain. PBS, *Scientific American* and every other pro-evolution propaganda machine have failed to identify any evidence that might strengthen this straw link.

## New evidence: hemoglobin not the result of common ancestry after all[9]

A 2010 paper published in the prestigious *Proceedings of the*

4.  Bergman, J., "Does gene duplication provide the engine for evolution?," *JoC* **20**(1):99–104, 2006, creation.com/gene-duplication.

5.  Liu, Y. and Moran, D., "Do new functions arise by gene duplication?," *JoC* **20**(2):82 89, 2006; creation.com/gene-duplication2.

6.  Liu, Y., "The immunoglobulin heavy chain gene family and gene duplication," *JoC* **22**(3):18–20, 2008; creation.com/immunoglobulin.

7.  Kihm, A. et al., "An abundant erythroid protein that stabilizes free α-haemoglobin," *Nature* **417**(6890):758–763, 13 June 2002; comment by Luzzatto, L. and Notaro, R., Haemoglobin's chaperone, *Nature* **417**(6890):703–705, 13 June 2002.

8.  See Aw, S.-E., "The Origin of Life: A Critique of Current Scientific Models," *JoC* **10**(3):300–314, 1996.

9.  "Vertebrates not 'one blood' after all," *Creation* **33**(1):9, 2011.

*National Academy of Sciences (USA)* claims hemoglobin evolved not once, but twice—completely independently of each other. Scientists analyzed the genes of jawless and jawed vertebrates and concluded these two groups used completely different proteins as templates for their different types of hemoglobin.

The old evolutionary tale was much simpler and much more likely to happen (if evolution could happen). But now they explain this by *convergence*—when two unrelated creatures share a similar trait. The trait therefore had to evolve twice. Evolving hemoglobin *once* by random mutation and selection is already stretching credulity to the limit, but *twice* ... ?

Similar 'convergences' are found repeatedly throughout life, with more and more instances uncovered all the time. See for example the discussion on the alleged missing link, *Tiktaalik*, page 144. This undermines evolution because it unites living things in a way that can't be explained by common descent. Rather, it speaks of a single Creator of life, who made all things to resist evolutionary explanations.

# Chapter 6

# Argument: Common Design Points to Common Ancestry

*Evolutionists say, 'Studies have found amazing similarities in DNA and biological systems—solid evidence that life on Earth has a common ancestor.'*

## Common structures = common ancestry?

In most arguments for evolution, the debater assumes that common physical features, such as five fingers on apes and humans, point to a common ancestor in the distant past. Darwin mocked the idea (proposed by Richard Owen on the PBS dramatization of his encounter with Darwin on the *Beagle*) that common structures (homologies) were due to a common creator rather than a common ancestor.

But the common designer explanation makes much more sense of the findings of modern geneticists, who have discovered just how *different* the genetic blueprint can be behind many apparent similarities in the anatomical structures that Darwin saw. *Genes* are inherited, not structures *per se*. So one would expect the similarities, if they were the result of evolutionary common ancestry, to be produced by a common genetic program (this may or may not be the case for common design). But in many cases, this is clearly not so. Consider the example of the five digits of both frogs and humans—the human embryo develops a bony plate, then material between the digits dissolves; in frogs, the digits grow outwards from buds (see diagram, below). This strongly argues against the 'common ancestry' evolutionary explanation for the similarity.

The PBS program and other evolutionary propagandists claim that the DNA code is universal, and proof of a common ancestor. But this is false—there are exceptions, some known since the 1970s, not only in mitochondrial but also nuclear DNA sequencing.[1] An example is *Paramecium*, where a few of the 64 codons code for different amino acids. More examples are being found constantly. The Discovery Institute has pointed out this clear factual error in the PBS program.[2] Also, some

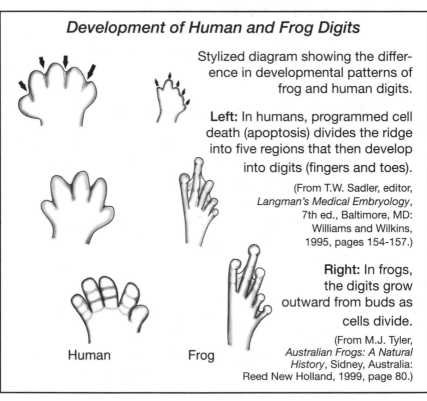

### *Development of Human and Frog Digits*

Stylized diagram showing the difference in developmental patterns of frog and human digits.

**Left:** In humans, programmed cell death (apoptosis) divides the ridge into five regions that then develop into digits (fingers and toes).

(From T.W. Sadler, editor, *Langman's Medical Embryology*, 7th ed., Baltimore, MD: Williams and Wilkins, 1995, pages 154-157.)

**Right:** In frogs, the digits grow outward from buds as cells divide.

(From M.J. Tyler, *Australian Frogs: A Natural History*, Sidney, Australia: Reed New Holland, 1999, page 80.)

Human          Frog

1. See Sarfati, J., "DNA: marvellous messages or mostly mess?," *Creation* **25**(2):26–31, 2003, creation.com/message.

2. Press release, "PBS Charged with 'False Claim' on 'Universal Genetic Code'," 10 September 2001, reviewevolution.com/press/pressRelease_FalseClaim.php.

organisms code for one or two extra amino acids beyond the main 20 types.[3]

The reaction by the PBS spokeswoman Eugenie Scott showed how the evolutionary establishment is more concerned with promoting evolution than scientific accuracy. Instead of conceding that the PBS show was wrong, she attacked the messengers, citing statements calling their (correct!) claim "so bizarre as to be almost beyond belief." Then she even implicitly conceded the truth of the claim by citing this explanation: "Those exceptions, however, are known to have derived from organisms that had the standard code."

To paraphrase: "It was wrong to point out that there really are exceptions, even though it's true; and it was right for the PBS to imply something that wasn't true because we can explain why it's not always true."

But assuming the truth of Darwinism as 'evidence' for their explanation is begging the question. There is no experimental evidence, since we lack the DNA code of these alleged ancestors. There is also the theoretical problem that if we change the code, then the wrong proteins would be made, the organism would die—so once a code is settled on, we're stuck with it. The Discovery Institute also demonstrated the illogic of Scott's claim.[4] Certainly most of the code is universal, but this is best explained by common design. Of all the millions of genetic codes possible, ours, or something almost like it, is optimal for protecting against errors.[5] But the exceptions thwart evolutionary explanations.

---

3. Certain Archaea and eubacteria code for 21st or 22nd amino acids, selenocysteine and pyrrolysine  see Atkins, J.F. and Gesteland, R., "The 22nd amino acid," *Science* **296**(5572):1409–10, 24 2002; commentary on technical papers on pp. 1459–62 and 1462–66.

4. Press release, Offscreen, "'Evolution' Spokesperson Tries to Tar Scientific Critics who are Ignored," 20 September 2001, reviewevolution.com/press/pressRelease_ScientistsTar.php.

5. Knight, J., "Top translator," *New Scientist* **158**(2130):15, 18 1998. Natural selection cannot explain this code optimality, since there is no way to replace the first functional code with a 'better' one without destroying functionality.

## DNA comparisons—subject to interpretation

*Scientific American* repeats the common argument that DNA comparisons help scientists to reconstruct the evolutionary development of organisms:

> Macroevolution studies how taxonomic groups above the level of species change. Its evidence draws frequently from the fossil record and DNA comparisons to reconstruct how various organisms may be related. [*SA* 80]

DNA comparisons are just a subset of the *homology* argument, which makes just as much sense in a biblical framework.[6] A *common designer* is another interpretation that makes sense of the *same* data. An architect commonly uses the same building material for different buildings, and a car maker commonly uses the same parts in different cars. So we shouldn't be surprised if a Designer for life used the same biochemistry and structures in many different creatures. Conversely, if all living organisms were totally different, this might look like there were *many* designers instead of one.

Since DNA codes for structures and biochemical molecules, we should expect the most similar creatures to have the most similar DNA. Apes and humans are both mammals with similar shapes, so both have similar DNA. We should expect humans to have more DNA similarities with another mammal like a pig than with a reptile like a rattlesnake. And this is so. Humans are very different from yeast but they have some biochemistry in common, so we should expect human DNA to differ more from yeast DNA than from ape DNA.

So the general pattern of similarities need not be explained by common-ancestry (evolution). Furthermore, there are some puzzling anomalies for an evolutionary explanation—similarities between organisms that evolutionists don't believe are closely related. For example, hemoglobin, the complex molecule that carries oxygen in blood and results in its red color, is found in

---

6. See Bergman, J., "Does homology provide evidence of evolutionary naturalism?" *JoC* **15**(1):26–33, 2001, creation.com/homology2.

vertebrates. But it is also found in *some* earthworms, starfish, crustaceans, molluscs and even in some bacteria. An antigen receptor protein has the same unusual single chain structure in camels and nurse sharks, but this cannot be explained by a common ancestor of sharks and camels.[7] And there are many other examples of similarities that cannot be due to evolution.

## Debunking the 'molecular clock'

*Scientific American* repeats the common canard that DNA gives us a 'molecular clock' that tells us the history of DNA's evolution from the simplest life form to mankind:

> Nevertheless, evolutionists can cite further supportive evidence from molecular biology. All organisms share most of the same genes, but as evolution predicts, the structures of these genes and their products diverge among species, in keeping with their evolutionary relationships. Geneticists speak of the 'molecular clock' that records the passage of time. These molecular data also show how various organisms are transitional within evolution. [*SA* 83]

The molecular clock depends on the Neutral Theory of Molecular Evolution, invented around 1968 by Motoo Kimura (1924–1994). This asserts that most evolutionary change at the molecular level is caused by genetic drift of selectively neutral mutations. Population geneticists had previously worked out that there was too little time to generate all the genome via natural selection. A deduction from neutral theory is that over 90% our genome is "junk DNA", which has now been junked itself (see page 121).

Actually, the molecular clock has many other problems for the evolutionist.[8] Not only is it based on flimsy support, and has

---

7.  *Proceedings of the National Academy of Sciences* 95:11,804; cited in *New Scientist* **160**(2154):23, 3 October 1998.

8.  There are also problems with it in analyzing human origins. Geneticist Dr Robert Carter shows that the popular Recent African Origins (RAO) theory is on tenuous ground largely because it relies on neutral evolution: "The Neutral Model of evolution and recent African origins," *JoC* **23**(1):70–77, 2009; and "Mitochondrial diversity within modern human

the anomalies and common designer arguments I mentioned above, but it actually supports a creation of distinct types within ordered groups, not continuous evolution, as non-creationist microbiologist Dr Michael Denton pointed out in *Evolution: A Theory in Crisis*. For example, when comparing the amino acid sequence of cytochrome C of a bacterium (a prokaryote) with such widely diverse eukaryotes as yeast, wheat, silkmoth, pigeon and horse, all of these have practically the same percentage difference with the bacterium (64–69%). There is no intermediate cytochrome between prokaryotes and eukaryotes, and no hint that the 'higher' organism such as a horse has diverged more than the 'lower' organism such as the yeast.

The same sort of pattern is observed when comparing cytochrome C of the invertebrate silkmoth with the vertebrates lamprey, carp, turtle, pigeon and horse. All the vertebrates are equally divergent from the silkmoth (27–30%). Yet again, comparing globins of a lamprey (a 'primitive' cyclostome or jawless fish) with a carp, frog, chicken, kangaroo and human, they are all about equidistant (73–81%). Cytochrome C's compared between a carp and a bullfrog, turtle, chicken, rabbit and horse yield a constant difference of 13–14%. There is no trace of any transitional series of cyclostome → fish → amphibian → reptile → mammal or bird.

Another problem for evolutionists is how the molecular clock could have ticked so evenly in any given protein in so many different organisms (despite some anomalies discussed earlier which present even more problems). For this to work there must be a constant mutation rate per unit *time* over most types of organism. But *observations* show that there is a constant mutation rate per *generation*, so it should be much faster for organisms with a fast generation time, such as bacteria, and much slower for elephants. In insects, generation times range from weeks in flies to many years in cicadas, and yet there is no evidence that flies are more diverged than cicadas. So evidence is *against* the theory that the observed patterns are due to mutations accumulating over time as life evolved.

population," *Nucleic Acids Research* 35(9):3039–3045, 2007 | doi:10.1093/nar/gkm207.

# Chapter 7

# Argument: "Bad Design" is Evidence of Leftovers from Evolution

*Evolutionists say, 'Nature is filled
with evidence of bad design—obvious
leftovers from our evolutionary past,
such as "junk DNA," vestigial organs
and eye imperfections.'*

To answer alleged 'bad design' arguments, there are two principles to consider:

1. Do we have all the information/knowledge on the issue?

2. Could this particular biological system have gone downhill since the Fall?[1]

Related evolutionary arguments are used to attack so-called vestigial organs (see Appendix 1, page 203), the panda's thumb and so-called 'junk' DNA.

## The inverted eye—example of bad design?

Kenneth Miller, the Roman Catholic evolutionist who is featured prominently on PBS 1 claims that the eye has 'profound optical imperfections', so is proof of 'tinkering' and 'blind' natural selection. Miller hasn't presented an argument *for* evolution *per se* at all—because he presents no step-by-step way for the retina to have evolved—but it is purely an attack on a designer. This is of

---

1. See also my later books *By Design*, ch. 12, 2008; and *Greatest Hoax on Earth?* ch. 15, 2010.

course also an attack on Miller's own Darwinian version of 'god', one who has chosen to create indirectly (via evolution).

Miller raised the old canard of the backwardly wired vertebrate retina, as he has done elsewhere. The narrator even claimed that the eye's 'nerves interfere with images', and that the so-called 'blind spot' is a serious problem. But these arguments have been refuted before, as shown below.[2]

It would be nice if anti-creationists actually learned something about the eye before making such claims (Miller is unqualified in both physical optics and eye anatomy), or even showed that the eye didn't function properly as a result. In fact, any engineer who designed something remotely as good as the eye would probably win a Nobel Prize! If Miller and the PBS producers disagree, then I challenge them to design a better eye with all the versatility of the vertebrate eye (colour perception, resolution, coping with range of light intensity, night vision as well as day vision, etc.)! And this must be done under the constraints of embryonic development.

The retina can detect a single photon of light, and it's impossible to improve on this sensitivity! More than that, it has a *dynamic range* of 10 billion ($10^{10}$) to one; that is, it will still work well in an intensity of 10 billion photons. Modern photographic film has a dynamic range of only 1,000 to one. Even specialist equipment hasn't anywhere near the dynamic range of the eye, and I have considerable experience in state-of-the-art supersensitive photomultipliers. My Ph.D. thesis and published papers in secular journals largely involve a technique called *Raman spectroscopy*, which analyses extremely weak scattering at a slightly different frequency from that of the incident laser radiation. The major equipment hazard for Raman spectroscopists is scanning at the incident frequency—the still weak Rayleigh scattering at the same frequency would blow the photomultiplier (the newer ones have an automatic shut-off). I managed to safely scan the Rayleigh line (for calibration) only by using filters to attenuate the intensity of light entering the photomultiplier by a factor of $10^{-7}$ to $10^{-8}$. But having to take such an extreme safety precaution made me

---

2.   See Sarfati, J., "Fibre optics in eye demolish atheistic 'bad design' argument," *Creation* **31**(1):45–47, 2008; creation.com/fibreoptic.

envious and admiring of the way the eye is so brilliantly designed to cope with a far wider range of intensities.

Another amazing design feature of the retina is the signal processing that occurs even before the information is transmitted to the brain, in the retinal layers between the ganglion cells and the photoreceptors. For example, a process called *edge extraction* enhances the recognition of edges of objects. Dr John Stevens, an associate professor of physiology and biomedical engineering, pointed out that it would take "a minimum of a hundred years of Cray [supercomputer] time to simulate what takes place in your eye many times each second."[3] And the retina's analog computing needs far less power than the digital supercomputers and is elegant in its simplicity. Once again, the eye outstrips any human technology, this time in another area.

Someone who *does* know about eye design is the ophthalmologist Dr George Marshall, who said:

> The idea that the eye is wired backward comes from
> a lack of knowledge of eye function and anatomy.[4]

He explained that the nerves could not go behind the eye, because that space is reserved for the choroid, which provides the rich blood supply needed for the very metabolically active retinal pigment epithelium (RPE). This is necessary to regenerate the photoreceptors, and to absorb excess heat. So it is necessary for the nerves to go in front instead. The claim on the program that they interfere with the image is blatantly false, because the nerves are virtually transparent because of their small size and also having about the same refractive index as the surrounding vitreous humour. In fact, what limits the eye's resolution is the diffraction of light waves at the pupil (proportional to the wavelength and inversely proportional to the pupil's size); so alleged improvements of the retina would make no difference.

It's important to note that the 'superior' design of Miller with the (virtually transparent) nerves behind the photoreceptors

3.   Byte, April 1985.

4.   Marshall, G. (interviewee), "An eye for creation," *Creation* **18**(4):20–21, 1996; creation.com/marshall.

would require either:

- The choroid in front of the retina—but the choroid is opaque because of all the red blood cells, so this design would be as useless as an eye with a hemorrhage!

- Photoreceptors not in contact with the RPE and choroid at all—but if our eyes lost this ability to absorb heat, then it would probably take months before we could drive after we were photographed with a flashbulb.

Some evolutionists claim that the cephalopod eye is somehow 'right', i.e. with nerves behind the receptor, and the program showed photographs of these creatures (e.g. octopus, squid) during this segment. But no one who has actually bothered to study these eyes could make such claims with integrity. In fact, cephalopods don't see as well as humans, and the octopus eye structure is totally different and much simpler. It's more like 'a compound eye with a single lens'.[5]

Ophthalmologist Peter Gurney gives a detailed response to the question "Is the inverted retina really 'bad design'?"[6] He addresses the claim that the blind spot is bad design, by pointing out that the blind spot occupies only 0.25% of the visual field, and is far (15°) from the visual axis so that the visual acuity of the region is only about 15% of the foveola, the most sensitive area of the retina right on the visual axis. So the alleged defect is only theoretical, not practical. The blind spot is not considered handicap enough to stop a one-eyed person from driving a private motor vehicle. The main problem with only one eye is the lack of stereoscopic vision.

The program also alleges that the retina is badly designed because it can detach and cause blindness. But this doesn't happen with the vast majority of people, indicating that the

5.　Budelmann, B.U., "Cephalopod sense organs, nerves and brain," 1994; in Pörtner, H.O., O'Dor, R.J. and Macmillan, D.L., ed., *Physiology of cephalopod molluscs: lifestyle and performance adaptations*, Gordon and Breach, Basel, Switzerland, p. 15, 1994.

6.　Gurney, P., "Is Our 'Inverted' Retina Really 'Bad Design'?" *JoC* **13**(1):37–44, 1999, revised December 2008, creation.com/retina.

design is pretty good. In fact, retinal detachment is more due to the vitreous ('glassy') humour liquefying from its normally fairly rigid gel state with advancing age. Then the remaining gel pulls away from the retina, leaving tiny holes, so the other liquefied humour can lift off the retina. So one recent treatment is draining the liquid and injecting magnetized silicone gel, which can be moved into place with a magnetic field, to push the retina back and block the holes.[7] The occasional failures in the eye with increasing age reflect the fact that we live in a fallen world—so what we observe today may have deteriorated from the original physically perfect state, where for example deterioration with age didn't occur.

## Fibre optic plate

The above section explains why the vertebrate retina must be wired the way it is. But scientists at Leipzig University have recently shown that the vertebrate eye has an ingenious feature that overcomes even the slight disadvantage of the transparent nerves in front of the light receptors [the "carpet of massed wires" that Dawkins complains about].[8]

The light is collected and funnelled through the nerve net to the receptors by the *Müller glial cells*, which act as *optical fibres*. Each cone cell has one Müller cell guiding the light to it, while several rods can share the same Müller cell.

Müller cells in the eye working as optical fibres

The Müller cells work almost exactly like a *fibre optic plate* that optical engineers can use to transmit an image with low distortion without using a lens. The cells even have the right variation in

7.   *New Scientist* **174**(2338):18, 13 April 2002.

8.   Franze, K. *et al.*, "Müller cells are living optical fibers in the vertebrate retina," Proc. Nat. Acad. Sci. USA, 10.1073/pnas.0611180104,  7 May 2007; www.pnas.org/cgi/content/abstract/0611180104v1.

refractive index for "image transfer through the vertebrate retina with minimal distortion and low loss."

Indeed, Müller cells are even better than optical fibres, because they are funnel-shaped, which collects more light for the receptors. The wide entrances to Müller cells cover the entire surface of the retina, so collect the maximum amount of light.

One of the research team, Andreas Reichenbach, commented: "Nature is so clever. This means there is enough room in the eye for all the neurons and synapses and so on, but still the Müller cells can capture and transmit as much light as possible."[9]

## New discovery: Müller cells enhance sharpness

In fact, Müller cells are even more than waveguides. In 2010, researchers Amichai Labin and Erez Ribak at the Technion-Israel Institute of Technology in Haifa found that the Müller cells are much more than that. They said:

> The retina is revealed as an optimal structure designed for improving the sharpness of images. ... The fundamental features of the array of glial cells are revealed as an optimal structure designed for preserving the acuity of images in the human retina. It plays a crucial role in vision quality, in humans and in other species.[10]

One reason is that images can be distorted by light 'noise', i.e. light that is reflected several times within the eye instead of coming directly through the pupil. But the Müller cells transmit the direct light strongly to the rods and cones, while the noise leaks out. This makes the images sharper.

Another problem with lenses is that they are basically prisms joined face-to-face, and have a tendency to separate the colours. This is called chromatic aberration. Expensive cameras have

---

9. Sheriff, L., "Living optical fibres found in the eye: Moving light past all those synapses," *The Register*, 20007; www.theregister. co.uk/2007/05/01/eye_eye/.

10. Labin, A.M. and Ribak, E.N., "Retinal glial cells enhance human vision acuity," *Physical Review Letters* **104**, 16, April 2010 | DOI:10.1103/ PhysRevLett.104.158102.

multiple lenses to try to avoid this problem. But "Müller cells' wide tops allow them to 'collect' any separated colours and refocus them onto the same cone cell, ensuring that all the colours from an image are in focus."[11]

Furthermore, the Müller cells are tuned to the visible region of the spectrum, and leak out other wavelengths, minimizing radiation and heat damage.

The researchers say:

> In this study, wave propagation methods allowed us to show that light guiding within the retinal volume is an effective and biologically convenient way to improve the resolution of the eye and reduce chromatic aberration. We also found that the retinal nuclear layers, until now considered a source of distortion, actually improve the decoupling of nearby photoreceptors and thus enhance vision acuity. Although this study was performed on data from human retinas and eyes, most of its consequences are valid for eyes with other retinal structure and different optics. They are also valid for the more common case of eyes without a central fovea.

*New Scientist* reports:

> "It suggests that light-coupling by Müller cells is a crucial event that contributes to vision as we know it," says Kristian Franze, a neurophysicist at the University of Cambridge and co-author of the 2007 study. "This work nicely complements our experimental data."

### Evolutionists dogmatically hang on to dud argument

It's notable that Kate McAlpine, writing in *New Scientist*, which is overtly anti-Christian,[12] had to admit, "It looks wrong, but the strange, 'backwards' structure of the vertebrate retina actually improves vision," after admitting that *New Scientist* had listed the backwardly wired eye as one of evolution's biggest 'mistakes.'

---

11.   McAlpine, K., "Evolution gave flawed eye better vision," *New Scientist* **206**(2759), 8 May 2010.

12.   Sarfati, J., "Refutation of New Scientist's Evolution: 24 myths and misconceptions," creation.com/24myths, 21 January 2009.

Yet not willing to junk a defunct evolutionary argument, she brings up the same man who made the claim in the PBS series:

> However, Kenneth Miller, a biologist at Brown University in Providence, Rhode Island cautions that this doesn't mean that the backwards retina itself helps us to see. Rather, it emphasises the extent to which evolution has coped with the flawed layout. "The shape, orientation and structure of the Müller cells help the retina to overcome one of the principal shortcomings of its inside-out wiring," says Miller.

First, he fails to address the important reasons for the backwardly-wired eye retina; second, he fails to show why it is a bad design anyway, especially given the newly discovered advantages of the wave guiding. Last, it is absurd given that the researchers think that this 'flawed' layout might help to improve camera design! Evidently he is not willing to give up one of his favorite evolutionary arguments, just because of a little thing like scientific evidence.[13]

## Panda's 'thumb'

Evolutionists have long cited the panda's clumsy-looking 'thumb' as evidence of evolution, rather than intelligent design. Gould even wrote a book called *The Panda's Thumb: More Reflections in Natural History* (1980) which says that the panda's thumb "wins no prize in an engineer's derby."[14]

On closer inspection, however, there is nothing clumsy at all about the panda's design.[15] Instead, the 'thumb' is part of an elaborate and efficient grasping structure that enables the panda to strip leaves from bamboo shoots.[16]

---

13. See also "Müller cells refuting Dawkins: feedback"—refuting atheopathic critics such as P.Z. Myers, creation.com/mueller-feedback, 3 July 2010.

14. Gould, S.J., *The Panda's Thumb: More Reflections in Natural History*, W.W. Norton & Co., New York, p. 24, 1980.

15. See Woodmorappe, John, "The Panda thumbs its nose at the dysteleological arguments of the atheist Stephen Jay Gould," *JoC* **13**(1):45–48, 1999, creation.com/pandathumb.

16. Endo, H. *et al.*, "Role of the giant panda's 'pseudo-thumb,'" *Nature*

Claims that the panda's thumb is some kind of non-designed 'contraption' is a smokescreen to distract from the real question—that evolution simply does not explain how life could start in a pond and finish with a panda.

## 'Junk' DNA

As we pointed out on page 111, the idea of "junk DNA" was first a deduction from evolution: natural selection could not have generated all the genome in the time available, so over 90% must be "junk". So often when evolutionists discover new strands of DNA that have no known function, they like to describe it as 'junk' DNA that is a leftover of evolution.

## Introns

One supposed place to find 'junk DNA' was the parts that did not seem to code for proteins. The genes of organisms more complex than bacteria contains regions called *exons* that code for proteins, and non-coding regions called *introns*. So the introns are removed and the exons are 'spliced' together to form the mRNA (messenger RNA) that is finally decoded to form the protein. Richard Roberts and Phillip Sharp won the 1993 Nobel Prize in Physiology and Medicine for discovering introns in 1977.

This also requires elaborate machinery called a *spliceosome*. This assembles on the intron, chops it out at the right place—the introns have signals at both ends, so are not functionless by definition—and joins the exons together. This must be in the right direction and place, because it makes a huge difference if the exon is joined even one letter off. Many human genetic diseases are caused by mutations at the splice sites.

But it's absurd, even on the face of it, that more complex organisms should evolve such elaborate machinery to splice the introns if they were really useless. Rather, natural selection would favour organisms that did *not* have to waste resources processing a genome filled with 98% of junk. And there have been many uses for junk DNA discovered, such as the overall genome structure and regulation of genes, so it is also likely that it could have enabled rapid post-Flood diversification.[17] Also, damage to introns can be disastrous—one example was deleting four 'letters' in the centre of an intron, preventing the spliceosome from binding to it, resulting in the intron being read into the protein, which interfered with the special shape required for its function.[18] Also, introns interfere with imprinting, the process by which only certain maternal or paternal genes are expressed, not both. Expression of both genes results in a variety of diseases and cancers.[19]

Furthermore, in 2010, Brendan Frey and colleagues at the University of Toronto discovered the 'splicing code', which controls the way certain pieces of RNA transcripts of the DNA code are spliced out.[20] This enables the exons within individual "genes" to be included in multiple proteins, and explains why humans have only about 20,000 genes yet make over 100,000 proteins, which surprised those who decoded the human genome. But thanks to the information decoded by the splicing code, "three neurexin genes can generate over 3,000 genetic messages that help control the wiring of the brain," according to Frey.[21] Geneticist Robert Carter summarizes:

> This splicing code must account for 1) the complex combinations of exons needed to create hundreds of thousands of proteins from tens of thousands of protein genes, 2) the variation in splicing from cell to cell needed to account for the different proteins expressed in different cell types, and 3) changes in splicing patterns over time as the organism proceeds from fertilized egg to adult (since not all genes are active at all stages in the life cycle). All

---

17. For an overview, see Walkup, L., "Junk DNA: evolutionary discards or God's tools?" *JoC* **14**(2):18–30, 2000, creation.com/junk-dna.

18. Cohen, P., "New genetic spanner in the works," *New Scientist* 173(2334):17, 16 March 2002.

19. Batten, Don, "Junk" DNA (again), *JoC* **12**(1):5, April 1998, creation.com/junk-dna-again.

20. Barash, Y., et al., "Deciphering the splicing code," *Nature* **465**:53–59, 2010 | doi:10.1038/nature09000.

21. "Researchers crack 'Splicing Code', solve a mystery underlying biological complexity," *Science News*, sciencedaily.com, 6 May 2010.

this information must be coded in the genome, but it also cannot interfere with the protein-coding domains. Thus, most of this information must reside within the introns and in the spaces between genes.[22]

But some of this information also lies in the protein-coding regions, because they contain splicing signals as well. So these parts of the DNA "message" are akin to a sequence of Latin alphabet letters that read coherently in both English and the unrelated language Finnish.

## Most of the genome is shown to be transcribed![23]

In 2007, the ENCODE (Encyclopedia of DNA Elements) project then reported on a detailed study of the RNA transcripts from only 1% of the human genome. This overturned much of the prevailing thinking about junk DNA. In particular, rather than only 2% of the genome being coding, they inferred that about 93% of the genome is transcribed (that is, copied to RNA).[24, 25] Further study may even raise this number even higher.

ENCODE found that exons are not gene-specific but are modules that can be joined to many different RNA transcripts. One exon can be used in combination with up to 33 different genes located on 14 different chromosomes. This means that one exon can specify one part shared in common by many different proteins.

ENCODE also discovered that DNA is even more efficient as an information storage medium. Not just one strand, but *both* strands (sense and anti-sense) of the DNA are fully transcribed.

22. Carter, R.W., "Splicing and dicing the human genome. Scientists begin to unravel the splicing code," creation.com/splicing, 1 July 2010.

23. After Williams, A., "Astonishing DNA complexity uncovered," creation.com/dnacomplex, 2007.

24. Birney, E. *et al.*, "Identification and analysis of functional elements in 1% of the human genome by the ENCODE pilot project," *Nature* **447**: 799–816, 2007.

25. Kapranov, P., Willingham, A.T. and Gingeras, T.R., "Genome-wide transcription and the implications for genomic organization," *Nature Reviews Genetics* **8**: 413–423, 2007.

And transcription proceeds not just one way but both backwards and forwards.

Furthermore, the introns turn out to be far more important than the exons, in that more of their DNA appears in RNA transcripts. The regions coding for proteins are transcribed on average in *five* different overlapping and interleaved ways. The 'non-coding' regions turn out to be transcribed on average in *seven* different overlapping and interleaved ways. Since there is about 33 times as much DNA in the introns as the exons, this means that the 'junk DNA' is about 50 times more active than the protein-coding regions.[26]

## Mattick vindicated

Dr John Mattick of the University of Queensland in Brisbane, Australia, published a number of papers arguing that the non-coding DNA regions, or rather their non-coding RNA 'negatives,' are important components of a complicated genetic network, or an advanced operating system.[27,28,29] In 2003, he lamented how the idea that non-protein-coding DNA was just junk had greatly harmed science:

> The failure to recognize the full implications of [non-protein-coding DNA] may well go down as one of the biggest mistakes in the history of molecular biology.[30]

A severe critic of Mattick's theory, Jean-Michel Claverie of CNRS, France's national research institute in Marseilles, said something very revealing:

> I don't think much of this work. In general, all these

26. Williams, A., "Astonishing DNA complexity update," creation.com/DNAupdate, 2007.

27. Mattick, J.S. "Non-coding RNAs: The architects of eukaryotic complexity," *EMBO Reports* **2**:986–991, November 2001.

28. Cooper, M., Life 2.0, *New Scientist* **174**(2346):30–33, 8 June 2002.

29. See also Sarfati, J., "DNA: marvellous messages or mostly mess?" *Creation* **25**(2):26–31, 2003; creation.com/message.

30. Mattick, J., cited in Gibbs, W.W., "The unseen genome: gems among the junk," *Scientific American* **289**(5):26–33, November 2003.

global ideas don't travel very far because they fail to take into account the most basic principle of biology: things arose by the additive addition of evolution of tiny subsystems, not by global design. It is perfectly possible that one intron in one given gene might have evolved—by chance—some regulatory property. It is utterly improbable that all genes might have acquired introns for the future property of regulating expression.

Two points to note:

1.  This agrees that if the intron system really is an advanced operating system, it really would be irreducibly complex, because evolution could not build it stepwise.

2.  It illustrates the role of materialistic assumptions behind evolution. Usually, atheists such as Dawkins use evolution as 'proof' for their faith; in reality, evolution is deduced from their assumption of materialism!

Similarly, while many have used 'junk' DNA as 'proof' of evolution, Claverie is using the assumption of evolution as 'proof' of its junkiness! This is again a parallel with vestigial organs. In reality, evolution was used as a proof of their vestigiality, and hindered research into their function. Claverie's attitude could likewise hinder research into the networking capacity of non-coding DNA.

The ENCODE project's discovery of the extent of RNA transcription and the later discovery of the splicing code vindicates Mattick's claim, and by Claverie's own reasoning, discredits evolution

## Electric protection of DNA?

DNA is actually a very unstable molecule (and RNA is even more so), so it's highly implausible that it could have arisen in a hypothetical primordial soup. One report on a newly discovered repair enzyme said:

> "There is a general belief that DNA is 'rock solid'—extremely stable," says Brandt Eichman, associate

professor of biological sciences at Vanderbilt, who directed the project. "Actually DNA is highly reactive."

On a good day about one million bases in the DNA in a human cell are damaged. These lesions are caused by a combination of normal chemical activity within the cell and exposure to radiation and toxins coming from environmental sources including cigarette smoke, grilled foods and industrial wastes.[31,32]

One major source of DNA damage is free radicals. They attack DNA by stealing an electron from (i.e. oxidizing) one of the bases—the chemical 'letters' of the DNA code. The resulting electron 'hole' can hop along the DNA, behaving like a positive electric current.

But Jacqueline Barton's group at the California Institute of Technology reported that about half of the 'junk' DNA comprises pairings between the 'letters' A and T (the bases adenine and thymine), and this blocks this damaging electrical current. These pairings act as insulators or 'electronic hinges in a circuit' to protect essential genes from electrical damage from free radicals attacking a distant part of the DNA.[33]

The Barton Group also showed that DNA uses its electrical properties for protection. At the edge of some genes, there is a string of G 'letters' (the base guanine). They readily absorb the electron hole, so the electron hole moves along until it reaches this string of Gs. This deflects the damage from the parts of the DNA that code for proteins.[34] This is very much like the principle behind galvanized iron. Here, a coating of a more reactive and less

31. "Newly Discovered DNA Repair Mechanism," *Science News*, sciencedaily.com, 5 October 2010.

32. Sarfati, J., "New DNA repair enzyme discovered," creation.com/dna-repair, 7 December 2010.

33. Coglan, A., Electric "DNA: There's another information superhighway lurking in our genes," *New Scientist* **161**(2173):19, 13 February 1999; citing Nunez, M.E., Hall, D.B. and Barton, J.K., *Chemistry & Biology* **6**(2):85, 1999.

34. Lawton, G., "Live wire," *New Scientist* **177**(2386):38–39, 15 March 2003, after Delaney, S. and Barton, J.K., "Charge transport in DNA duplex/ quadruplex conjugates," *Biochemistry* **42**:14159–14165, 2003.

important metal, zinc, sacrificially takes all the oxidation, thus protecting the iron from rusting.

Evolutionists have produced a long list of examples of 'bad design', but nothing on the list stands up under scrutiny.

# Chapter 8

# Argument: The Fossil Record Supports Evolution

*This chapter discusses the fossil record, how interpretations are strongly influenced by one's assumptions, how it lacks the transitional forms evolution predicts, and discusses in detail some of the common evolutionary claims. Note: the human fossil record is not covered in this chapter, but in ch. 12.*

## The fossil record: prediction of evolution?

*S*cientific American claims that the placement of fossils in the geologic record was predicted by evolution and is strong evidence for it. But it can't even keep the 'facts' straight.

> But one should not—and does not—find modern human fossils embedded in strata from the Jurassic period (65 million years ago). [*SA* 80]

Of course I don't believe the millions of years in the first place but I know enough to know that *Scientific American* made a blooper even under its own perspective. Evolutionists assign the date of 65 Ma to the K–T (Cretaceous-Tertiary boundary) *not* the Jurassic period, which is alleged to have been 208–144 Ma. After I first posted a rebuttal on the CMI website, *Scientific American* corrected their error on the web version of the article.

Actually, even if they found human fossils deeply buried in the earth that would contradict their assumptions about the geologic column and the fossil record, evolutionists could easily accommodate such 'out of place fossils', as they have with living specimens of the 'ancient' coelacanth fish and 'dinosaur era' Wollemi Pine. These recent finds are just as sensational—from an evolutionary paleontologist's perspective—as finding a living dinosaur. Since the materialistic paradigm (interpretive framework) is all important, evolutionists would be able to explain an 'old' human fossil by 'reworking' (displacing from the initial burial depth), or may even reassign such bones to another creature, since after all 'we know' that humans can't be that deep in the fossil record!

A good example of reworking is the famous fossil footprints at Laetoli, Africa, of an upright walking biped—the University of Chicago's Dr Russell Tuttle has shown that these are the same sorts of prints as made by habitually barefoot humans. But since they are dated at millions of years prior to when evolutionists believe modern humans arrived, they are regarded as australopithecine prints, by definition, even though australopithecine foot bones are substantially different from human ones. And then in an amazing twist, the same prints are held up as evidence that australopithecines walked upright like humans—regardless of the fact that other aspects of their anatomy indicate otherwise.[1]

In spite of evolutionists' assumptions to the contrary, the fossil order can be explained in a creationist framework, which actually avoids some of the contradictions of the evolutionary view.[2] The 'fountains of the great deep' (Genesis 7:11) would logically have buried small seafloor creatures first. Water plants would generally be buried before coastal and mountain plants.

---

1.   Another good example of how a researcher's presuppositions can lead to all sorts of special pleading is the explaining away of clear evidence for a fossil belemnite. See Walker, T., "Fossil flip-flop," *Creation* **22**(1):6, 1999, creation.com/fossil-flip-flop.

2.   See Snelling, A., "Where are all the human fossils?," *Creation* **14**(1):28–33, 1991, creation.com/human-fossils; Woodmorappe, J., "The Fossil Record: Becoming More Random All the Time," *JoC* **14**(1):110–116, 1999, creation. com/the-fossil-record.

Land creatures would be buried last, especially the mammals and birds that could escape to higher ground. The more intelligent creatures would find a way to escape until the very end, leaving their bodies nearer the surface, where post-Flood erosion would destroy most evidence of their existence. Humans would have been most resilient of all, clinging to debris and rafts, before they died of exposure; their floating bodies would have made easy meals for scavenging fish. Most mammal and human fossils are post-Flood.

## ARGUMENT: Multitudes of Transitional Fossils Exist

*Evolutionists say, 'Paleontologists have found many examples of transitional fossils for creatures such as birds, whales and horses.'*

Evolutionists recognize a serious threat to their whole argument—evolution predicts innumerable transitional forms, yet all they have are a handful of debatable ones. Yet they are unwilling to admit to the magnitude of the problem. *Scientific American* states the problem in this way, and it answers with an unsupportable claim that there are numerous intermediate fossils:

> *13.  Evolutionists cannot point to any transitional fossils—creatures that are half reptile and half bird, for instance.*
>
> Actually, paleontologists know of many detailed examples of fossils intermediate in form between various taxonomic groups. [SA 83]

Actually, Charles Darwin was worried that the fossil record did not show what his theory predicted:

> Why is not every geological formation and every stratum full of such intermediate links? Geology assuredly does not reveal any such finely-graduated organic chain; and this is the most obvious and serious objection which can be urged against the theory.[3]

---

3.    Darwin, C., *Origin of Species*, 6th ed. 1872, reprinted 1902, John Murray,

More recently, Gould said:

> The extreme rarity of transitional forms in the fossil record persists as the trade secret of paleontology.[4]

But modern evolutionists, including Gould, have asserted that there are nevertheless some transitional forms, but they always seem to name the same handful of disputable ones, instead of the many that Darwin hoped for. It's the same with *Scientific American* below.

## Bird evolution

> One of the most famous fossils of all time is *Archaeopteryx*, which combines feathers and skeletal structures peculiar to birds with features of dinosaurs. [*SA* 83]

This hardly qualifies for a fossil 'intermediate in form'; it is more like a mosaic or chimera like the platypus. Alan Feduccia, a world authority on birds at the University of North Carolina at Chapel Hill and an evolutionist himself, admits:

> Paleontologists have tried to turn *Archaeopteryx* into an earth-bound, feathered dinosaur. But it's not. It is a bird, a perching bird. And no amount of 'paleobabble' is going to change that.[5]

*Archaeopteryx* had fully-formed flying feathers (including asymmetric vanes and ventral, reinforcing furrows as in modern flying birds), the classical elliptical wings of modern woodland birds, and a large wishbone for attachment of muscles responsible for the down stroke of the wings.[6] Its brain was essentially that of a flying bird, with a large cerebellum and visual cortex. The fact that it had teeth is irrelevant to its alleged transitional status—a

---

London, p. 413.

4.  Gould, S.J., "Evolution's erratic pace," *Natural History* **86**(5):14, 1977.

5.  Cited in Morell, V., "*Archaeopteryx:* Early Bird Catches a Can of Worms," *Science* **259**(5096):764–65, 5 February, 1993.

6.  Feduccia, A., "Evidence from claw geometry indicating arboreal habits of *Archaeopteryx*," *Science* **259**(5096):790–793, 5 February, 1993.

number of extinct birds had teeth, while many reptiles do not. Furthermore, like other birds, both its maxilla (upper jaw) and mandible (lower jaw) moved. In most vertebrates, including reptiles, only the mandible moves.[7] Finally, *Archaeopteryx* skeletons had pneumatized vertebrae and pelvis. This indicates the presence of both a cervical and abdominal air sac, i.e. at least two of the five sacs present in modern birds. This in turn indicates that the unique avian lung design was already present in what most evolutionists claim is the earliest bird.[8]

The fossil bird known as *Archaeopteryx* is among the most prized relics in the world.

*(Artist's impression of Archeaopteryx by Steve Cardno.)*

*Scientific American* hurls more elephants without examples.

> A flock's worth of other feathered fossil species, some more avian and some less, has also been found. [*SA* 83]

But the *Creation Ministries International* website (creation. com) has documented that two famous alleged feathered dinosaurs are 'dated' younger than their supposed descendant *Archaeopteryx* and more likely to be flightless birds (*Protarchaeopteryx* and *Caudipteryx*). Another famous example, *Archaeoraptor*, was a fake.

---

7. See Wieland, C., "Bird Evolution flies out the window," *Creation* **16**(4):16–19, June 1994, creation.com/bird-evo.

8. Christiansen, P. and Bonde, N., "Axial and appendicular pneumaticity in *Archaeopteryx*," *Proceedings of the Royal Society of London*, Series B. **267**:2501–2505, 2000.

## Horse evolution

The horse sequence is another popular evidence of a fairly complete series of transitional fossils. *Scientific American* boldly claims:

> A sequence of fossils spans the evolution of modern horses from the tiny *Eohippus*. [*SA* 83]

Like the *Archaeopteryx*, however, this doesn't hold up. Even informed evolutionists regard horse evolution as a bush rather than a sequence. But the so-called *Eohippus* is properly called *Hyracotherium*, and has little that could connect it with horses at all. The other animals in the 'sequence' actually show hardly any more variation between them than that *within* horses today. One non-horse and many varieties of the true horse kind does not a sequence make.[9]

## Mollusks

*Scientific American* makes another false claim:

> Fossil seashells trace the evolution of various mollusks through millions of years. [*SA* 83]

Again, what does this mean? One must wonder if the author of the article believes the old *Ostrea/Gryphaea* story, i.e. that a flat oyster evolved into more and more coiled forms till it coiled itself shut. Once this was regarded as a key proof of an evolutionary lineage in the fossil record. But now it seems that the coiling was the oyster's built-in programming to respond to the environment, or *ecophenotypic change*.[10] So the anti-creationist neo-catastrophist geologist Derek Ager wrote:

> It must be significant that nearly all the evolutionary stories I learned as a student, from Trueman's *Ostrea/Gryphaea* to Carruthers' *Zaphrentis delanouei*, have now been "debunked". Similarly, my own experinece

9.   See Sarfati, J., "The Non-evolution of the horse," *Creation* **21**(3):28–31, 1999, creation.com/evolutionofthehorse.

10.  Machalski, M., "Oyster life positions and shell beds from the Upper Jurassic of Poland," *Acta palaeontologica Polonica* **43**(4):609–634, 1998.

[*sic*] of more than twenty years looking for evolutionary lineages among the Mesozoic Brachiopoda has proved them equally elusive.[11]

*Scientific American* closes its argument about transitional fossils with these mocking words about their demands for a truly transitional fossil:

> Creationists, though, dismiss these fossil studies. They argue that *Archaeopteryx* is not a missing link between reptiles and birds—it is just an extinct bird with reptilian features. They want evolutionists to produce a weird, chimeric monster that cannot be classified as belonging to any known group. [*SA* 83]

Actually, as stated, of the few transitional forms usually touted, most are actually chimeras. No, creationists have long simply requested a sequence of creatures with certain characteristics consistently following a series, e.g. 100% leg/0% wing → 90% leg/10% wing → ... 50% leg/50% wing... → 10% leg/90% wing → 0%leg/100% wing.

> Even if a creationist does accept a fossil as transitional between two species, he or she may then insist on seeing other fossils intermediate between it and the first two. These frustrating requests can proceed *ad infinitum* and place an unreasonable burden on the always incomplete fossil record. [*SA* 83]

First, this again charges creationists with believing in fixity of species, which is rather a belief held by compromisers like Hugh Ross. Instead, creationists ask for transitions between major categories, such as between non-living matter and the first living cell, single-celled and multicelled creatures, and invertebrates and vertebrates. The gaps between these groups should be enough to show that molecules-to-man evolution is without foundation.

Second, this is hardly a new charge when made of fossils transitional between two phyla, for example, and it is hardly

---

11. Ager, D., "The nature of the fossil record," *Proceedings of the Geologists' Association* **87**(2):131–160, 1976.

unreasonable for creationists to point out that there are still two large gaps rather than one even larger gap.[12]

## Whale evolution?

Whale evolution is a topic that deserves special attention. *Scientific American* claims:

> Whales had four-legged ancestors that walked on land, and creatures known as *Ambulocetus* and *Rodhocetus* helped to make that transition [see 'The Mammals That Conquered the Seas,' by Kate Wong; *Scientific American*, May]. [*SA* 83]

Here is an especially serious example of 'hurling elephants' by completely ignoring the fragmentary nature of the evidence.

This was a tricky problem for Darwin, but nevertheless he still had faith that whales evolved from land mammals. The paleontologist Phil Gingerich of the University of Michigan has publicly said he agrees that "it's a real puzzle how whales originally evolved." But on the PBS *Evolution* series, he gives the impression that his fossil finds have gone a long way towards solving this puzzle.

## Pakicetus

Gingerich discovered in Pakistan a few skull fragments of a wolf-like creature that allegedly had an inner ear like a whale's. But this is far from conclusive. There wasn't any post-cranial skeleton found, so we haven't the faintest idea how it moved. However, this didn't stop Gingerich from writing an article for schoolteachers with an illustration of an animal swimming and catching fish, and looking convincingly like an intermediate between land animals and whales. He also claimed, "In time and in its morphology, *Pakicetus* is perfectly intermediate, a missing link between earlier land mammals and later, full-fledged whales."[13] The diagram (right) shows the glaring contrast between reconstruction and reality.

---

12. Woodmorappe, J., "Does a 'transitional form' replace one gap with two gaps?" *JoC* **16**(2):5–6, 2000, creation.com/onegap.

13. Gingerich, P., "The Whales of Tethys," *Natural History*, p. 86, April 1994.

## Pakicetus: "Evidence" for Whale Evolution?

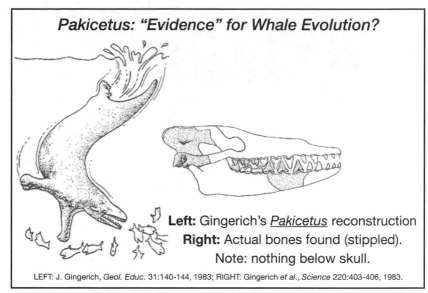

**Left:** Gingerich's *Pakicetus* reconstruction
**Right:** Actual bones found (stippled).
Note: nothing below skull.

LEFT: J. Gingerich, *Geol. Educ.* 31:140-144, 1983; RIGHT: Gingerich *et al.*, *Science* 220:403-406, 1983.

New research since the PBS series was produced has blown away this reconstruction. This demonstrates an oft-repeated phenomenon in evolutionary paleontology. Many of the alleged transitional forms are based on fragmentary remains, which are therefore open to several interpretations, based on one's axioms. Evolutionary bias means that such remains are often likely to be interpreted as transitional, as with Gingerich, and is also prevalent in ape-man claims. But when more bones are discovered, then the fossils nearly always fit one type or another, and are no longer plausible as transitional. It's also notable that alleged intermediate forms are often trumpeted in the media, while retractions are usually muted or unpublicized.

A prominent whale expert, Thewissen, and colleagues unearthed some more bones of *Pakicetus*, and published their work in the journal *Nature*.[14] The commentary on this paper in the same issue[15] says, "All the postcranial bones indicate that pakicetids were land mammals, and ... indicate that the animals

14. Thewissen, J.G.M., Williams, E.M, Roe, L.J. and Hussain, S.T., "Skeletons of terrestrial cetaceans and the relationship of whales to artiodactyls," *Nature* **413**:277–281, 20, 2001.

15. Muizon, C. de, "Walking with whales," *Nature* **413**:259–260, 20, 2001 (comment on Ref. 120).

***Pakicetus***

*(Illustration: Carl Buell; www.neoucom.edu/Depts/Anat/Pakicetid.html)*

were runners, with only their feet touching the ground.' (See illustration above) This is very different from Gingerich's picture of an aquatic animal! But the evolutionary bias is still clear, describing *Pakicetus* as a 'terrestrial cetacean' and saying, 'The first whales were fully terrestrial, and were even efficient runners.' But the term 'whale' becomes meaningless if it can describe land mammals, and it provides no insight into how true marine whales supposedly evolved.

Also, 'solid anatomical data' contradict previous theories of whale ancestry. A Reuters news article reported in September 2001:[16]

> Until now paleontologists thought whales had evolved from mesonychians, an extinct group of land-dwelling carnivores, while molecular scientists studying DNA were convinced they descended from artiodactyls [even-toed ungulates].
>
> "The paleontologists, and I am one of them, were wrong," Gingerich said.

Such candor is commendable, and it shows the fallacy of trusting alleged 'proofs' of evolution. Pity that Gingerich is still committed to materialistic evolutionism.

---

16. "Fossil Finds Show Whales Related to Early Pigs," *Reuters*, 19 September 2001.

## Ambulocetus

*Ambulocetus* is another popular example of a 'missing link', featured prominently in anti-creationist propaganda, such as the book *Finding Darwin's God,* by Kenneth Miller—the 'Christian evolutionist' who starred in PBS 1 (see page 35). On page 265 of his book, Miller claimed, 'the animal could move easily both on land and in water', and presented a drawing of a complete skeleton and a reconstructed animal. But this is misleading, bordering on deceitful, and indicative of Miller's unreliability, because there was no indication of the fact that far fewer bones were actually found than appear in his diagram. Crucially, the all-important pelvic girdle was not found (see diagram, below). Without this, it's presumptuous for Miller to make that proclamation. His fellow evolutionist Annalisa Berta pointed out:

### Ambulocetus: Missing Link?

**Top:** *Ambulocetus* skeleton, as drawn in Miller's book.
**Middle:** *Ambulocetus* reconstruction, as drawn in Miller's book.
**Bottom:** Actual bones found (shaded). Note missing pelvic girdle.

... since the pelvic girdle is not preserved, there is no direct evidence in *Ambulocetus* for a connection between the hind limbs and the axial skeleton. This hinders interpretations of locomotion in this animal, since many of the muscles that support and move the hindlimb originate on the pelvis.[17,18]

## Basilosaurus

This serpentine and fully aquatic mammal has been known since the 19th century, but Gingerich discovered something new in some specimens in the Sahara Desert. The PBS narrator pointed out that this desert area was under water once, and he described a 100-mile stretch of layered sandstone called the 'valley of the whales' and allegedly 40 million years old. The narrator theorizes that this valley was once a protected bay where whales came to give birth and to die. Here Gingerich discovered what he alleged were a pelvis, leg bones and a knee cap, so he said they were evidence of 'functioning legs' and 'dramatic proof that whales were once fully four-legged mammals.'

But this contradicts other evolutionists, including Gingerich himself! For example, the National Academy of Science's *Teaching about Evolution and the Nature of Science* claimed, "they were thought to be non-functional" (page 18 of the NSA book), and Gingerich himself said elsewhere 'it seems to me that they could only have been some kind of sexual and reproductive clasper.'[19] So these bones can be explained as a design feature, while the interpretation as 'legs' reflects evolutionary wishful thinking.[20]

17. Berta, A., "What is a Whale?" *Science* **263**(5144):180–181, 1994; perspective on Thewissen, J.G.M., Hussain, S.T. and Arif, M., "Fossil evidence for the origin of aquatic locomotion in Archeocete whales," same issue, pp. 210—212.

18. See also Batten, D., "A Whale of a Tale?," *JoC* **8**(1):2–3, 1994, creation.com/ambulo, includes the addendum addressing claims of subsequent *Ambulocetus* bones and their (ir)relevance to evolution.

19. *The Press Enterprise*, 1 July 1990, A-15.

20. Another urban myth about whales found with legs is punctured in Wieland, C., "The strange tale of the leg on the whale," *Creation* **20**(3): 10–13, 1998, creation.com/whaleleg.

## Whale evolutionary sequence?

The PBS program claims that there is a series including *Ambulocetus, Rhodocetus,* etc., where the nostrils supposedly migrate to the back of the head. *Teaching about Evolution and the Nature of Science* contains a diagram (below) on page 18. But when the mammal-to-whale series is examined, the sequence is not as smooth as they imply. For instance, this diagram failed to

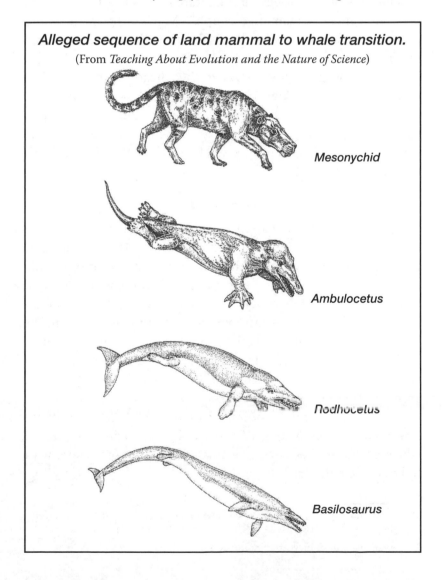

*Alleged sequence of land mammal to whale transition.*
(From *Teaching About Evolution and the Nature of Science*)

Mesonychid

Ambulocetus

Rodhocetus

Basilosaurus

indicate that *Basilosaurus* is actually about 10 times longer than *Ambulocetus* (and the fragmentary nature of the remains has been discussed already).

Another problem is that *Basilosaurus* has a number of features that mean it could not possibly have been ancestral to modern whales, e.g. body shape, skull structure and tooth shape.

There is certainly no support for the program's claim, "front legs became fins, rear legs disappeared, bodies lost fur and took on their familiar streamlined shape." Waving the magic wand of mutation/selection is hardly sufficient without an observable *mechanism* that would effect these changes.

John Woodmorappe analysed the alleged transitions and found that their various characteristics did not change in a consistent direction. Rather, they are chimeras—non-whales with a few minor cetacean 'modules', inconsistent with the evolutionary prediction of a nested hierarchy but consistent with a common designer.[21]

## Locomotion

PBS 2 also claims support for a transition from the way the mammal-to-whale fossil links moved. Marine mammals move through the water with vertical undulating movements of the spine, just as many fast-running mammals do on land. Fish move with sideways undulations instead. But this could be another common design feature of mammals, like milk or hair. It's also doubtful whether this is a unique prediction of evolution; if whales used side-to-side movements, evolutionists could presumably have 'predicted' this because the tails of land animals also swish sideways.

My book *Refuting Evolution*, written to rebut *Teaching about Evolution and the Nature of Science*, has a chapter on alleged whale evolution that covers all this section in more detail, with full documentation.[22]

---

21. Woodmorappe, J. "Walking whales, nested hierarchies and chimeras: Do they exist?" *JoC* **16**(1):111–119, 2002, creation.com/walkingwhales.

22. Available online at creation.com/rech5.

## Tetrapod evolution?

Tetrapods are animals with four limbs, i.e. amphibians, reptiles, birds and mammals.  In 1995, Shubin and Ted Daeschler found in Pennsylvanian cliffs a shoulder bone of a tetrapod allegedly 370 million years old.

Cambridge University paleontologist Jenny Clack found an early tetrapod hand in Greenland, called *Acanthostega*. Supposedly this creature had gills, a fish-like tail, paddle-shaped fins, and a hand with fingers.  It's notable that evolutionists often appeal to the common pentadactyl 5-digit pattern as evidence for their common ancestry from a 5-digited creature. Yet the allegedly ancestral *Acanthostega* had *eight digits not five*, something not mentioned by the program!

On PBS 2, Clack said this refuted the usual textbook theory that fish evolved limbs for a selective advantage because they were being stranded in drying pools.  Rather, the limbs evolved before they crawled on the land, while they were still aquatic. The selective advantage was the ability to escape the weird and wonderful predatory fish that lived during this time (called the Devonian Period).

Shubin stressed that 'evolution wasn't trying to do this', and later the PBS program claimed, 'we're here through chance coincidences'. This should make it clear that evolution, as believed by evolutionists, is not 'progressive' and shows no sign of a divine guiding hand, as pointed out on pages 34 and 168 ff.

Shubin also highlighted the common limb pattern between tetrapods, illustrated by fish and humans having the sequence one bone/two bones/small bones/rods (digits).  But this fails to explain the totally different developmental sequence, as previously explained.

## Tiktaalik

After the first edition of this book was published, Shubin and Daeschler discovered *Tiktaalik roseae* in 2006,[23,24,25] supposedly closing a gap between *Panderichthys* and *Acanthostega*. Richard Dawkins proclaimed:

> *Tiktaalik* is the perfect missing link—perfect, because it almost exactly splits the difference between fish and amphibian, and perfect because it is missing no longer.[26]

Dawkins is following the infectious enthusiasm of evolutionary palaeontologists who claimed that this is "a link between fishes and land vertebrates that might in time become as much of an evolutionary icon as the proto-bird *Archaeopteryx*."[27]

But how intermediate is it really? One of those enthusiastic palaeontologists cited above, Jennifer Clack (University of Cambridge, UK), admitted:

> There remains a large morphological gap between them and digits as seen in, for example, *Acanthostega*: if the digits evolved from these distal bones, the process must have involved considerable developmental repatterning. …
>
> Of course, there are still major gaps in the fossil record. In particular we have almost no information about the step between *Tiktaalik* and the earliest

---

23. Daeschler, E.B., Shubin, N.H. and Jenkins, F.A., Jr., A Devonian tetrapod-like fish and the evolution of the tetrapod body plan, *Nature* **440** (7085):757–763, 6 April 2006.

24. Shubin, N.H., Daeschler, E.B. and Jenkins, F.A., Jr, "The pectoral fin of *Tiktaalik roseae* and the origin of the tetrapod limb," *Nature* **440** (7085):764-771, 6 April 2006.

25. See also Sarfati, J., "Tiktaalik—a fishy 'missing link,'" *JoC* **21**(1): 53–57, 2007; creation.com/tiktaalik.

26. Dawkins, R., *The Greatest Show on Earth*, p. 169, 2009. See also the refutation: Sarfati, J. *The Greatest Hoax on Earth?* Creation Book Publishers, 2010.

27. Ahlberg, P.E. and Clack, J.A., "Palaeontology: A firm step from water to land," *Nature* **440**(7085):747–749, 6 April 2006.

tetrapods, when the anatomy underwent the most drastic changes, or about what happened in the following Early Carboniferous period, after the end of the Devonian, when tetrapods became fully terrestrial.[28]

Indeed, *Tiktaalik's* fins that were supposed to have become legs were not connected to the main skeleton, so could not have supported its weight on land. The discoverers claim that they could have helped to prop up the body as the fish moved along the sea bottom,[49] but evolutionists had similar high hopes for the coelacanth fin. However, when a living coelacanth (*Latimeria chalumnae*) was discovered in 1938, the fins turned out not to be used for walking but for deft maneuvring when swimming.

Thus all the claims about *Tiktaalik* are mere smokescreens, exaggerating mere tinkering around the edges while huge gaps remain unbridged by evolution. And it is hardly unreasonable for creationists to point out that there are still two large gaps rather than one huge gap.[29]

The series of corresponding limbs does *not* appear to show the clear progression. It is not obvious that the *Panderichthys* limb belongs in between the adjacent ones in the series. It has fewer small bones. And a later study indeed argued that *Panderichthys'* fin may be *closer* to tetrapods in morphology than *Tiktaalik*.[30,31]

## Common features NOT due to inheritance from common ancestor

The *Tiktaalik* discoverers themselves appear to recognize that there are some anomalies:

28   Ahlberg, P.E. and Clack, J.A., "Palaeontology: A firm step from water to land," *Nature* 440(7085):747749, 6 April 2006, doi:10.1038/440747a.

29.  Woodmorappe, J., "Does a 'transitional form' replace one gap with two gaps?," *JoC* 14(2):5–6, 2000; creation.com/onegap.

30.  Boisvert, C.A., Mark-Kurik, E. and Ahlberg, P.E., "The pectoral fin of *Panderichthys* and the origin of digits," *Nature* 456:636–638, 2008, doi:10.1038/nature07339.

31.  Doyle, S., "*Panderichthys*—a fish with fingers?" creation.com/panderichthys, 9 December 2008.

In some features, *Tiktaalik* is similar to rhizodontids such as *Sauripterus*. These similarities, which are probably homoplastic, include the shape and number of radial articulations on the ulnare, the presence of extensive and branched endochondral radials, and the retention of unjointed lepidotrichia.

'Homoplastic' essentially means 'convergent' or 'analogous', i.e. independently evolved to be similar because of a common function (such as the wings of pterosaurs, bats, birds and insects), rather than evolved from a common ancestor (homologous, as the pentadactyl limb is claimed to be). Homology is, however, alleged to be *the* evidence for evolution (despite many problems, as shown in ch. 6) But appealing to homoplasy is really *explaining away* evidence that doesn't fit the paradigm, and indeed such explaining away is ubiquitous (see also ch. 6). Two evolutionists admit:

> Disagreements about the probable homologous or homoplastic nature of shared derived similarities between taxa lie at the core of most conflicting phylogenetic hypotheses.[32]

In fact, when more characteristics than just one are analyzed, homoplasies become even more necessary to explain away anomalies. Another example is that the neck region of *Tiktaalik* is said to be homoplastic with that of *Mandageria*.[33]

In reality, *Tiktaalik* appears to be another *mosaic* or *chimera*, like *Archaeopteryx*. It has some fish-like aspects, some unique features such as the hyomandibula,[34] and some tetrapod-like features. Under an evolutionary scenario, this would mean that they are all at different stages of evolution. However, natural selection can only work on organisms as a *whole*, not on parts; therefore

---

32. Luckett, W.P. and Hong, N., "Phylogenetic relationships between the orders Artiodactyla and Cetacea," *J. Mammalian Evolution* **5**(2):130, 1998.

33. Johanson, Z., Ahlberg, P., Ritchie, A., "The braincase and palate of the tetrapodomorph sarcopterygian Mandageria fairfaxi: morphological variability near the fish-tetrapod transition," *Palaeontology* **46**:271–293, 2003.

34. The hyomandibula is a pair of deep bones or cartilage in the hyoid (neck) region in most fishes, which usually helps suspend the jaws.

a new trait cannot be selected for outside of the context of the whole organism. Moreover, mosaic evolution does not identify an evolutionary lineage; evolutionists have only identified traits that seem to change in complex, independent and contradictory ways in an evolutionary framework.[35] But a designer who worked with different modules could create different creatures with different *modules*, that fit no consistent evolutionary pattern.

## Polish footprints undermine story[36]

Tracks of footprints found on the surface of large limestone slabs from Zachelmie Quarry in the Holy Cross Mountains of Poland have turned the palaeontological world upside down.[37,38,39] This is because they are evidence of a 2-metre-long four-limbed walking creature 'dated' at 397 million years old. This predates all the alleged fish-to-tetrapod transitional forms, including the now-famous *Tiktaalik*, and the more fish-like *Panderichthys*, and is 12 million years older than the undoubted fish *Eusthenopteron*.

Other evolutionists were equally shocked, including the *Tiktaalik* enthusiasts of Ref. 57:

- "They force a radical reassessment of the timing, ecology and environmental setting of the fish-tetrapod transition, as well as the completeness of the body fossil record." [40]

- "[It] will cause a significant reappraisal of our understanding

35. Doyle, S., "*Tiktaalik*—sticking its head out of water?" creation.com/tiktaalik2, 12 December 2008.

36. Walker, T., "Tetrapods from Poland trample the *Tiktaalik* school of evolution," J. *Creation* 24(1):55–59, 2010; creation.com/tetrapod-footprints.

37. Niedzwiedzki, G., Szrek, P., Narkiewicz, K., Narkiewicz, M and Ahlberg, P., "Tetrapod trackways from the early Middle Devonian period of Poland," *Nature* 463(7227):43–48, 2010.

38. Editor's Summary, "Four feet in the past: trackways pre-date earliest body fossils," *Nature* 463(7227), 2010; nature.com/nature.

39. Bryne, J., "Four-legged creature's footprints force evolution rethink," livescience.com, 6 January 2010.

40. Niedzwiedzki, G., Szrek, P., Narkiewicz, K., Narkiewicz, M and Ahlberg, P., "Tetrapod trackways from the early Middle Devonian period of Poland," *Nature* 463(7227):43–48, 2010.

of tetrapod origins." [41]

- "We thought we'd pinned down the origin of limbed tetrapods. We have to rethink the whole thing." [42]

- "These results force us to reconsider our whole picture of the transition from fish to land animals."

- "[They] could lead to significant shifts in our knowledge of the timing and ecological setting of early tetrapod evolution."[43]

- "That's surprising, but this is what the fossil evidence tells us."[44]

Furthermore, the tracks look five-toed, although the paper reconstructs them as six- or seven-toed. If the prints rather than the reconstructions reflect reality, it would show 5-digited tetrapods long predating their alleged ancestors that had more digits, i.e. were 'less evolved'.

This all goes to show that grand claims and story-telling pass as evolutionary 'science' and just one small fossil discovery can undo years of 'rock-solid' evidence for evolution.

## Cambrian Explosion

During his appearance on PBS 2, Cambridge University paleontologist Simon Conway Morris explained that the Cambrian explosion was 'one of the greatest breakthroughs in the history of life.' Essentially all the different animal phyla (major groups) appeared abruptly, without any known transitional forms preceding them. According to evolutionary dating methods, this was about 500 million years ago. Morris acknowledged that Darwin recognized this as a problem for his

41. Editor's Summary, "Four feet in the past: trackways pre-date earliest body fossils," *Nature* **463**(7227), 2010; nature.com/nature.

42. Clack, J., cited in: "Curry, M., Ancient four-legged beasts leave their mark," *ScienceNOW Daily News*, sciencenow.sciencemag.org, 6 January 2010.

43. Roach, J., "Oldest land-walker tracks found—pushes back evolution," *National Geographic News*, nationalgeographic.com, 6 January 2010.

44. Paleontologist Philippe Janvier from the National Museum of Natural History, Paris, France; in: Amos, J., "Fossil tracks record 'oldest land-walkers," *BBC News*, news.bbc.co.uk, 6 January 2010.

theory, with animals appearing out of nowhere. Morris said, 'to a certain extent that is still a mystery.' Darwin predicted that animals diverged gradually from a common pattern, so there should be fossil examples of this divergence, while instead we see that the major differences arose abruptly at the beginning. Again, this is according to the evolutionary time frame; biblical creationists see the fossil record not as a time sequence but a sequence of burial by Noah's Flood and its after-effects.

Then the PBS program shifted to the Burgess Shale, with lots of bizarre creatures, e.g. one with five eyes, another worm-like creature with large spines, and still another with prongs around its mouth. But none of this showed what the Cambrian animals could have evolved from. Supposedly the evidence shows that evolution tinkered with a few basic body plans, but provides no evidence for their *origins*.

It should also be noted that, when geologists say life appeared suddenly during the Cambrian explosion without transitional forms, they're making a backhand admission of the paucity of transitional fossils.

## Ediacaran explosion

Many evolutionists have tried to excuse the lack of fossils for the alleged ancestors of the Cambrian animals by claiming that the conditions were unfavourable for fossilization. However, research on Precambrian formations has discovered conditions so favourable for fossilization that even many soft-bodied creatures have been found. A good example is the wide variety of creatures discovered from the 'Ediacaran Period' ('dated' at 635–542 Ma, and named after the Ediacara Hills of South Australia). Even though many Ediacaran fossils included soft bodied organisms, none are ancestral to the Cambrian creatures.[31] Indeed, recent research has even identified an 'Avalon Explosion', whereby:

> A comprehensive quantitative analysis of these fossils indicates that the oldest Ediacara assemblage—the Avalon assemblage (575 to 565 Ma)—already

encompassed the full range of Ediacara morphospace.[45]

So this hardly solves the problem for evolutionists—rather, they have *two* unrelated explosions of new creatures with no evidence of evolutionary ancestry.[46]

## Extinction!

The whole emphasis on extinction, such as PBS 3 on 'Extinction!' is rather strange. It hardly tells us anything to prove evolution *per se*. Rather, it says a lot about species *dying out*, which is hardly news to anyone, but it doesn't itself shed any light on how species *arose* in the first place. The PBS program makes plenty of *assertions* about new species diversifying to take the place of the old ones, but it offers no *evidence* of any mechanism how this could occur. It's just another example of how vacuous words can become when survivors of extinctions are called 'evolution's big winners'. How exactly does the word 'evolution' explain anything here? The only purpose seems to be to further the indoctrination of the public with the idea that it does. But really, saying 'history's big winners' or 'winners of the lottery of life' would be just as informative.

## Have most species become extinct?

PBS 3 repeated a common claim, that 95–99% of species have become extinct. However, the known record of extinct and extant species does not support this. The number of fossil species is estimated to be about 250,000, while there are about 3 million living 'species', or even more, depending on who's telling the story. But if this >95% claim were correct, we would expect many more fossil species than living ones.

The only plausible explanation is evolutionary bias. For evolution to be true, there would have been innumerable transitional forms between different types of creature. Therefore,

45. Shen, B., Dong, L., Xiao, S. and Kowalewski, M., "*The Avalon* explosion: evolution of Ediacara morphospace," *Science* **319**:81–84, 2008.

46. Doyle, S., creation.com/ediacaran-explosion, 5 March 2008.

for every known fossil species, many more must have existed to connect it to its ancestors and descendents. This is yet another example of evolutionary conclusions coming before the evidence. Really, the claim is an implicit admission that large numbers of transitional forms are predicted, which heightens the difficulty for evolutionists, given how few there are that even they could begin to claim were candidates.

## Mass extinctions

Supposedly there were five mass extinctions in Earth's history, caused by planet-wide catastrophes. The greatest was the Permian extinction about 250 million years ago, where 90% of species became extinct. The period allegedly represented by rock layers above the Permian, the Triassic, was almost void of life. But later, in the upper Triassic, the dinosaurs supposedly evolved. Alongside them were the mammal-like reptiles that supposedly evolved into mammals.

The best-known extinction was that of the dinosaurs, at the end of the Cretaceous, dated at 65 million years ago. Supposedly the small mammals, who kept out of sight when dinosaurs were around, managed to survive the catastrophe by hiding in burrows, while dinosaurs couldn't hide or protect their eggs. In the next period, the Tertiary, mammals are supposed to have diversified and filled the vacant niches.

The PBS program presents the usual meteorite impact theory as fact, i.e. a chunk of rock the size of Mt. Everest hit Earth at 25,000 mph. The many problems with this idea are ignored. For example:

- The extinction was not that sudden (using evolutionary/long age interpretations of the geological record). But the spread in the geological record makes sense if much of the sedimentary deposits were formed in Noah's Flood.

- Light-sensitive species survived.

- Extinctions don't correlate with crater dates, even given evolutionary dating assumptions.

- Modern volcanic eruptions don't cause global extinction patterns, even if they cause a temporary temperature drop.

- The iridium enrichment, supposedly a key proof of meteor impact, is not nearly as clearly defined as claimed.

- Drill cores of the apparent 'smoking gun' crater on the Yucatán peninsula in south-east Mexico do not support the idea that it is an impact crater.

- It seems that some scientists didn't speak out against the idea for fear of undermining the 'nuclear winter' idea, and being grouped with 'nuclear warmongers'.[47]

In general mass extinctions are explained as a house of cards collapsing, where each card represents a species. One species may collapse, but then all other species that depend on it, either directly or indirectly, will also collapse. Even without a catastrophe, there are many factors that can cause a 'bottom card' species to die out, e.g. a new predator or climatic change.

## Why bother preserving species?

All of this talk about fossils and extinctions causes a problem for evolutionists who are also rabid environmentalists. The PBS episode on extinction exposes this problem: first, it asserts that humans are just another species, then it insists that extinction is simply part of Earth's history, and finally it moralizes that humans should try to preserve other species. The narrator says that humans 'may be the asteroid that brings about the next mass extinction', and that we 'competed with other species and won.'

But if we're just another species, then why shouldn't we act like one? Why should we aid our competitors for survival, when other species act in self-interest? The only reason might be a practical one, that we might lose some species that are beneficial to us. But this is very different from a *moral obligation* to care for them. If we are all

---

47. See my analysis in "Did a meteor wipe out the dinosaurs? What about the iridium layer?," creation.com/iridium, after Officer, C. and Page, J., *The Great Dinosaur Extinction Controversy*, Helix Books, Massachusetts, 1996, reviewed by Wieland, C., *JoC* **12**(2):154–158, 1998, creation.com/dino-extinct.

rearranged pond scum, then talk of moral obligation is meaningless. Under a consistent evolutionary worldview, our moral sentiments are merely chemical motions in the brain that happened to confer a survival advantage in our alleged ape-like ancestors.

## Creationist explanation

As elaborated on pages 34 and 88, the Bible teaches that death is the 'last enemy', the result of Adam's sin, and is an intruder into God's very good creation. This is a problem for those who want to add millions of years to the Bible, and this program demonstrated just how much death is entailed by millions-of-years belief, because of the record of death (and disease, violence, etc.) the fossils portray.

Biblical creationists would explain much of the fossil record by the global Flood of Noah's day. However, this didn't directly cause any land vertebrates to become extinct, because each kind was represented on the Ark. But many became extinct in subsequent centuries, because of factors already well known to conservationists. But the Flood probably did cause many marine species to become extinct.

Creationists and evolutionists interpret the geological layers differently because of our different axioms. Evolutionists interpret the sequence of layers as a sequence of *ages* with different types of creatures; creationists interpret them as a sequence of *burial* by a global Flood and its after-effects. This makes better sense of phenomena such as 'living fossils' and finding creatures such as the coelacanth that isn't found in rocks 'dated' younger than 70 million years.

# UNIT 3

## CLAIM 3:

# "Problems" with Evolution are Illusionary

*Evolutionists argue that there are reasonable theories for even the biggest 'surprises' of evolution.*

# Chapter 9

# Argument: Probability of Evolution

*Evolutionists say, 'Biochemistry,
computer simulations and observations
of "natural" order (such as crystals and
snowflakes) show that evolution
is highly probable.'*

This chapter will examine several claims about the probability of evolution. I'll quote from points 7, 8 and 9 of *Scientific American*'s '15 Answers to Creationist Nonsense,' and then respond in turn. Each point in *Scientific American* gives a charge against evolution, followed by the magazine's attempted answer.

## Origin of Life

### 7. Evolution cannot explain how life first appeared on earth.

The origin of life remains very much a mystery, but biochemists have learned about how primitive nucleic acids, amino acids and other building blocks of life could have formed ... [*SA* 81]

Actually, they have found out how some major building blocks *cannot* be formed, e.g. cytosine. The proposed 'prebiotic' conditions that biochemists attempt to recreate in the laboratory are unrealistic because it is highly unlikely that the alleged 'precursor chemicals' could ever have concentrated sufficiently, and these chemicals would have undergone side reactions with other organic compounds. Cytosine is far too unstable, anyway, to have accumulated over 'deep time' because its half life is only 340 years at 25° C.[1]

> ... and organized themselves into self-replicating, self-sustaining units, ... [*SA* 81]

This is just bluff, since spontaneous polymerization is a major hurdle for non-living chemicals to overcome.[2] So is producing molecules all of one handedness.[3] Chemical evolutionists have yet to solve these problems, let alone produce any self-replicating system which has any relevance to cells.[4]

> ... laying the foundation for cellular biochemistry. Astrochemical analyses hint that quantities of these compounds might have originated in space and fallen to earth in comets, a scenario that may solve the problem of how those constituents arose under the conditions that prevailed when our planet was young. [*SA* 81]

Again, wishful thinking, partly motivated by the hopelessness of current theories about life spontaneously generating on Earth. There are several problems, including the following:[5]

- The amounts of these chemicals are tiny—far too low to contribute to biological processes.

---

1. Sarfati, J., "Origin of Life: Instability of building blocks," *JoC* **13**(2):124–127, 1999, creation.com/blocks.

2. Sarfati, J., "Origin of Life: The Polymerization Problem," *JoC* **12**(3):281–284, 1998, creation.com/polymer.

3. Sarfati, J., "Origin of Life: The Chirality Problem," *JoC* **12**(3):263–266, 1998, creation.com/chirality.

4. Sarfati, J., "Self-Replicating Enzymes?" *JoC* **11**(1):4–6, 1997, creation.com/replicating.

5. Sarfati, J., "Sugars from Space? Do they prove evolution?" *JoC* **16**(1):9–11, 2002, creation.com/sugars; "Did life's building blocks come from outer space?" "Amino acids from interstellar simulation experiments?" *JoC* **16**(2):17–20, 2002, creation.com/aminospace.

- The wide variety of compounds in itself counts as evidence against chemical evolution. Even with pure compounds used in experiments, the results are meagre, so how much worse would they be with the contaminated gunk produced in the real world?

- Sugars are very unstable, and easily decompose or react with other chemicals. This counts against any proposed mechanism to concentrate them to useable proportions.

- Living things require homochiral sugars, i.e. with the same 'handedness', but the ones from space would not have been.

- Even under highly artificial conditions, there is no plausible method of making the sugar ribose join to some of the essential building blocks needed to make DNA or RNA. Instead, the tendency is for long molecules to break down.

- Even DNA or RNA by themselves would not be life, since it's not enough just to join the bases ('letters') together, but the sequence must be meaningful—and this sequence is not a function of the chemistry of the letters.

- Even the correct letter sequence would be meaningless without elaborate decoding machinery to translate it. Unless the decoding machinery already existed, those instructions can never be read. Similarly, this book would be useless to a non-English-speaker, who may know the Roman alphabet but lacks knowledge of the code of the *English* language to convert letters into meaningful concepts.

> Creationists sometimes try to invalidate all of evolution by pointing to science's current inability to explain the origin of life. But even if life on earth turned out to have a nonevolutionary origin (for instance, if aliens introduced the first cells billions of years ago), evolution since then would be robustly confirmed by countless microevolutionary and macroevolutionary studies. [*SA* 81]

Here we go again with the bait-and-switch concerning the

meanings of evolution. Anyway, that downplays the real problem. Evolution is a pseudo-intellectual justification for materialism, because it purports to explain life without God. So materialism would be in great trouble if evolution had a problem right at the start ('chemical evolution'). After all, if the process can't even start, it can't continue.

## Evolution 'does not depend on chance'? Really?

*8. Mathematically, it is inconceivable that anything as complex as a protein, let alone a living cell or a human, could spring up by chance.*

Chance plays a part in evolution (for example, in the random mutations that can give rise to new traits), but evolution does not depend on chance to create organisms, proteins or other entities. Quite the opposite: natural selection, the principal known mechanism of evolution, harnesses nonrandom change by preserving 'desirable' (adaptive) features and eliminating 'undesirable' (nonadaptive) ones. [*SA* 81]

But the raw material on which natural selection acts is random copying errors (mutations). If evolution from goo-to-you were true, we should expect to find *countless* information-adding mutations. But we have not even found *one*. Even worse, it appears that mutations *damage* instead of improve the genome of an animal, meaning that mutation causes the breakdown of a species, not its evolution.[6]

It is misleading to claim that evolution does not depend on chance but instead it relies on 'nonrandom' natural selection. This ignores the fact that natural selection cannot explain the *origin* of *complex*, self-reproducing life forms—and evolutionists have no way to explain this essential step in the evolution of life.

---

6. Williams, A., "Mutations: evolution's engine becomes evolution's end," *JoC* 22(2):60–66, 2008, creation.com/evolutions-end; Sanford, J., *Genetic Entropy and the Mystery of the Genome*, FMS Publications, Waterloo, NY, 2008.

Incidentally, it's important to note that a *non-complex* life form is an impossibility, since it needs to have the ability to reproduce. Even the simplest known true self-reproducing organism, *Mycoplasma genitalium* (a parasitic bacterium, discussed on pages 97 ff.), has 482 genes with 580,000 'letters' (base pairs). But even this appears not to be enough to sustain itself without parasitizing an even more complex organism. Most likely, as discussed, the parasitism resulted from loss of some of the genetic information required to make some essential nutrients. Therefore a hypothetical first cell that could sustain itself would have to be even *more* complex.

> As long as the forces of selection stay constant, natural selection can push evolution in one direction and produce sophisticated structures in surprisingly short times. [*SA* 81]

An *example* would have been nice.

## Computer 'simulations' of evolution

*Scientific American* alludes to computer 'simulations' of evolution, although these are based on assumptions that do *not* parallel real life:

> As an analogy, consider the 13-letter sequence 'TOBEORNOTTOBE.' Those hypothetical million monkeys, each pecking out one phrase a second, could take as long as 78,800 years to find it among the 26¹³ sequences of that length. But in the 1980s Richard Hardison of Glendale College wrote a computer program that generated phrases randomly while preserving the positions of individual letters that happened to be correctly placed (in effect, selecting for phrases more like Hamlet's). On average, the program re-created the phrase in just 336 iterations, less than 90 seconds. Even more amazing, it could reconstruct Shakespeare's entire play in just four and a half days. [*SA* 81–82]

These computer programs have been widely popularized by the atheist Richard Dawkins, but are a lot of bluff. Such simulations, which Dawkins, and now *Scientific American*, propose as 'simulations' of evolution, work towards a known goal, so they are far from a parallel to real evolution, which has no foresight, hence a 'Blind Watchmaker'. The simulations also use 'organisms' with high reproductive rates (producing many offspring), high mutation rates, a large probability of a beneficial mutation, and a selection coefficient of 1 (perfect selection) instead of 0.01 (or less), which parallels real life more accurately. The 'organisms' have tiny 'genomes' with minute information content, so they are less prone to error catastrophe, and they are not affected by the chemical and thermodynamic constraints of a real organism.

*Journal of Creation* published an article about a realistic computer simulation, with a program downloadable from the CMI website,[7] which shows that the goal is *not* reached if realistic values are programmed, or it takes so long that it shows that evolution is impossible.[8,9,10,11]

Also, when it comes to the origin of *first* life, natural selection cannot be invoked, because natural selection is differential reproduction. That is, if it worked at all, it could only work on a living organism that could produce offspring. By its very definition it could not work on non-living chemicals.[12] Therefore chance *alone* must produce the precise sequences needed, so these simulations do not apply. And a further problem with the

7.   Batten, D. and Ey, L., "Weasel, a flexible program for investigating deterministic computer 'demonstrations' of evolution," *JoC* **16**(2):84–88, 2002, creation.com/weasel.

8.   For more information, see my refutation of Dawkins' book *Climbing Mt Improbable*, "Stumbling over the impossible," *JoC* **12**(1):29–34, 1998; creation.com/dawkins.

9.   Gitt, W., with Wieland, C., "Weasel Words," *Creation* **20**(4):20–21, 1998, creation.com/weasel-words.

10.  Truman, R., Dawkins' weasel revisited, *JoC* **12**(3):358–361, 1998, creation.com/dawkins-weasel-revisited.

11.  For a refutation of the whole idea of computer simulations of evolution, particularly in the guise of genetic algorithms, see Batten, D., "Genetic algorithms—do they show that evolution works?," creation.com/algorithm.

12.  Dobzhansky, T., "Synthesis of Nucleosides and Polynucleotides with Metaphosphate Esters," in Fox, S., ed., *The Origins of Prebiological Systems*, **299**:310, 1965.

alleged chemical soup is reversibility, intensifying the difficulty of obtaining the right sequence by chance.[13]

## Random order ≠ complexity

*Scientific American*'s next example of 'creationist nonsense' begins with shadow boxing against an argument that informed creationists don't make (see appendix on the Second Law of Thermodynamics). Then the article proceeds to reveal a common mistake that evolutionists make: assuming that the random occurrence of *order* (repetitive, low information) in nature, such as crystals and snowflakes, provides insight into the generation of *complexity* (nonrepetitive, high information).

> ### 9. The Second Law of Thermodynamics says that systems must become more disordered over time. Living cells therefore could not have evolved from inanimate chemicals, and multicellular life could not have evolved from protozoa.
>
> This argument derives from a misunderstanding of the Second Law. [*SA* 82]

It would be most surprising, in our experience, if an anti-creationist lacking training in physics or chemistry understood the Second Law himself. As will be shown, biologist John Rennie, who wrote the *Scientific American* article on 'creationist nonsense,' is no exception. I should say that Rennie's formulation of the creationist argument is not how informed creationists would argue—see Appendix 2, page 226.

> If it were valid, mineral crystals and snowflakes would also be impossible, because they, too, are complex structures that form spontaneously from disordered parts. [*SA* 82]

No, as usual, this anti-creationist confuses *order* (repetitive,

---

13. Grigg, R., "Could Monkeys Type the 23rd Psalm?" *Creation* **13**(1):30–33, 1990, creation.com/monkeys.

low information) with complexity (non-repetitive, high information). The difference between crystals in rocks and proteins in living organisms is profound. Break a crystal and you just get smaller crystals; break a protein and you don't simply get a smaller protein; rather you lose the function completely. Large crystals have low information content that is simply repeated, while the protein molecule isn't constructed simply by repetition. Those who manufacture proteins know that they have to add one amino acid at a time, and each addition has about ninety chemical steps involved.

> The Second Law actually states that the total entropy of a closed system (one that no energy or matter leaves or enters) ... [*SA* 82]

It's more usual for those qualified in physical chemistry to refer to this as an *isolated system*, and use the term *closed system* for one where energy but not matter can be exchanged with its surroundings.

> ... cannot decrease. Entropy is a physical concept often casually described as disorder, but it differs significantly from the conversational use of the word. [*SA* 82]

We totally agree, and point this out often.

> More important, however, the Second Law permits parts of a system to decrease in entropy as long as other parts experience an offsetting increase. Thus, our planet as a whole can grow more complex because the sun pours heat and light onto it, and the greater entropy associated with the sun's nuclear fusion more than rebalances the scales. Simple organisms can fuel their rise toward complexity by consuming other forms of life and nonliving materials. [*SA* 82]

This energy input is necessary *but not sufficient*. The proverbial bull in a china shop produces disorder, but if the same bull was harnessed to a generator, this energy could be directed into useful work. Similarly, living organisms have machinery to direct the energy from sunlight or food, including the ATP synthase enzyme. This is the world's tiniest motor, so tiny that $10^{17}$ could fit into a pinhead.[14,15,16] Paul Boyer and John Walker won a half share of the 1997 Nobel Prize for Chemistry for their proposal that the enzyme was a motor after the research in Ref. 14 confirmed it. But machinery presupposes teleology (purpose), which means that the machinery must have had an intelligent source.

14. Noji, H. et al., "Direct observation of the rotation of F1-ATPase," *Nature* **386**(6622):299–302. Comment by Block, S., "Real engines of creation," same issue, pp. 217–219, 1997.

15. Sarfati, J., "Design in Living Organisms: Motors," *JoC* **12**(1):3–5, 1998, creation.com/motor.

16. For a more recent and popular level article, see Thomas, B., "ATP synthase: majestic molecular machine made by a mastermind," *Creation* **31**(4):21–23, 2009; the online version creation.com/atp-synthase links to an animation CMI produced.

# Chapter 10

# Argument: Irreducible Complexity

*Evolutionists say, 'Examples of supposed "irreducible complexity" (such as the eye, the complex cell and the flagellum) can be explained.'*

T his chapter will examine how evolutionists respond to the 'irreducible complexity' argument in three areas: the eye, the complex cell and the flagellum. *Scientific American* states the problem this way:

> **14. Living things have fantastically intricate features—at the anatomical, cellular and molecular levels—that could not function if they were any less complex or sophisticated. The only prudent conclusion is that they are the products of intelligent design, not evolution.**

This 'argument from design' is the backbone of most recent attacks on evolution, but it is also one of the oldest. In 1802 theologian William Paley wrote that if one finds a pocket watch in a field, the most reasonable conclusion is that someone dropped it, not that natural forces created it there. By analogy, Paley argued, the complex structures of living things must be the handiwork of direct, divine invention. Darwin wrote *On the Origin of Species* as an answer to Paley: he explained how natural forces of selection, acting on inherited features, could gradually shape the evolution of ornate organic structures. [*SA* 83]

Indeed, Gould, who was an expert on the history of evolution, agreed that Darwin was writing to counter Paley. This is another way of saying that he had an anti-theistic agenda,[1,2] as discussed in Ch. 2. This doesn't stop many churchian academics kowtowing to every pronouncement made by Darwin and his God-hating successors, no matter what cost to Christianity.

A good recent example is BioLogos,[3] a theistic evolutionary organization. As Al Mohler, President of Southern Baptist Theological Seminary, pointed out in a reply to Karl Giberson, vice president of BioLogos:

> If your [Karl Giberson's] intention in [his book] *Saving Darwin* is to show "how to be a Christian and believe in evolution," what you have actually succeeded in doing is to show how much doctrine Christianity has to surrender in order to accommodate itself to evolution. In doing this, you and your colleagues at BioLogos are actually doing us all a great service. You are showing us what the acceptance of evolution actually costs, in terms of theological concessions.[4]

Another example is the Canadian dentist and theistic evolutionist Denis Lamoureux, supposedly an evangelical. One reviewer of his book *I Love Jesus & I Accept Evolution* (2009) wrote:

> I have to conclude that despite its irenic approach

1. Wieland, C., "Darwin's real message: Have you missed it?" *Creation* **14**(4):16–19, 1992, creation.com/realmessage.
2. Sarfati, J., "Review of Birkett, K., *The Essence of Darwinism*," 28 December 2001, creation.com/birkett.
3. See for instance Cosner, L., "Evolutionary syncretism," 7 September 2010, creation.com/biologos-evolutionary-syncretism.
4. Al Mohler, "On Darwin and Darwinism: An Open Letter to Professor Giberson," AlbertMohler.com, 26 August 2010. Giberson had published an abusive *ad hominem* piece on the secular liberal site *Huffington Post*.

and the undoubted expertise of its author, this book fails in its goal of reconciling biblical Christianity with modern evolutionary science. Nevertheless, it is very useful in this respect: it makes clear what price has to be paid in order to make peace with evolution, even if one takes a relatively conservative approach. The first casualties are the doctrines of biblical authority, clarity, and inerrancy, closely followed by the doctrine of original sin; and once those are sacrificed it's inevitable that more will follow, for no doctrine is an island. The doctrines of salvation by grace alone and justification by faith alone, to cite two examples, are intimately connected to the nature of the fall and its consequences.

The stakes are high. These are gospel issues. Lamoureux may well be correct about what it takes to accept evolution, as he defines it; but if he is, then precisely because I love Jesus, I cannot accept evolution. Fortunately, his scientific arguments put me under little pressure to do so.[5]

But in return, the militant atheists regard them as contemptuously as Lenin regarded his 'useful idiot'[6] allies in the West.[7] For example, Dawkins said:

> Oh, but of course, the story of Adam and Eve was only ever *symbolic*, wasn't it? *Symbolic*? So, in order to impress himself, Jesus had himself tortured and executed, in vicarious punishment for a *symbolic* sin

---

5. Anderson, J., www.discerningreader.com/, 4 June 2010.

6. The origin of this phrase was explained by conservative columnist Ken Blackwell as follows: "Beset by shortages, invading Germans, and civil war at home, Lenin presided over one famous Kremlin meeting during which he renewed his assurances that capitalism was on its last legs. 'We will hang all the capitalists,' Lenin pledged. His comrade Martov bitterly answered: 'Under our great new socialist government, we couldn't even find enough rope to hang them!' Lenin, ever humorless, responded: 'When I get ready to hang the capitalists, those useful idiots will sell me the rope—on credit.'" (patriotpost.us, 2 August 2010).

7. Sarfati, J., "The Skeptics and their 'Churchian' Allies," creation.com/iscast, November 1998.

committed by a *non-existent* individual? As I said, barking mad, as well as viciously unpleasant.[8]

Similarly, it's not surprising that an astute Christian blogger noted that BioLogos is having a diametrically opposite effect on the enemies of Christianity from what it intends:

> By your compromise, (A) you are not winning them over, but (B) are signalling to them that they are winning you over. They will simply wait you out, until you continue in your process of jettisoning everything the world hates about you as a Christian.
>
> After all, if they can get you to toss such a straightforward chapter, the rest should be child's play.[9]

## Could the eye have evolved?

It's interesting to note that the eye, which evolutionists claim is an example of 'bad design' leftover from evolution (previous chapter), presents their greatest challenge as an example of superb 'irreducible complexity' in God's creation. *Scientific American* says:

> Generations of creationists have tried to counter Darwin by citing the example of the eye as a structure that could not have evolved. The eye's ability to provide vision depends on the perfect arrangement of its parts, these critics say. Natural selection could thus never favor the transitional forms needed during the eye's evolution—what good is half an eye? Anticipating this criticism, Darwin suggested that even 'incomplete' eyes might confer benefits (such as helping creatures orient toward light) and thereby survive for further evolutionary refinement. [*SA* 83]

First, this overlooks the incredible complexity of even the simplest light sensitive spot. Second, it's fallacious to argue that

8. Dawkins, *The God Delusion*, p. 253, emphasis in original.
9. Dan Phillips, "A Coda on the Week's Discussion", Pyromaniacs blog, teampyro.blogspot.com, 26 June 2010.

51% vision would necessarily have a strong enough selective advantage over 50% to overcome the effects of genetic drift's tendency to eliminate even beneficial mutations.[10]

> Biology has vindicated Darwin: researchers have identified primitive eyes and light-sensing organs throughout the animal kingdom and have even tracked the evolutionary history of eyes through comparative genetics. (It now appears that in various families of organisms, eyes have evolved independently.) [*SA* 83]

*Scientific American* contradicts itself here. If the evolutionary history of eyes has been tracked though comparative genetics, then how is it that eyes have supposedly evolved independently? Actually, evolutionists recognize that eyes must have arisen independently at least 30 times because there is no evolutionary pattern to explain the origin of eyes from a common ancestor. What this really means is that since eyes cannot be related by common ancestor, and only materialistic explanations are allowed to explain their existence, hey presto, there's proof that they evolved independently!

## Simulation of eye evolution

PBS 1 goes to great lengths to convince us that the eye could have easily evolved. Dan Nilsson explained a simplistic computer simulation he published in a widely publicized paper.[11] Taking his cue from Darwin, who started with a light-sensitive spot when 'explaining' the origin of the eye, Nilsson's simulation starts with a light-sensitive layer, with a transparent coating in front and a light-absorbing layer behind.

Here is how the simulation proceeds. First, the light-sensitive layer bends gradually into a cup, so it can tell the direction of light rays increasingly well. This continues until it is curved into a hemisphere filled with the transparent substance. Second,

---

10. See my discussion about the evolution of the eye in "Stumbling over the impossible: Refutation of Climbing Mt Improbable," *JoC* **12**(1):29–34, 1998, creation.com/dawkins#eye.

11. Nilsson, D.-E. and Pelger, S., "A pessimistic estimate of the time required for an eye to evolve," *Proc. R. Soc. Lond.* B **256**:53–58, 1994.

bringing the ends together, closing the aperture, gradually increases the sharpness of the image, as a pinhole camera does, because a smaller hole cuts out light. But because of the diffraction of light if the hole is too small, there is a limit to this process. So third, the shape and refractive index gradient of the transparent cover change gradually to a finely focusing lens. Even if we were generous and presumed that such computer simulations really have anything to do with the real world of biochemistry, there are more serious problems.

However, the biochemist Michael Behe has shown that even a 'simple' light sensitive spot requires a dazzling array of biochemicals in the right place and time to function. He states that each of its 'cells makes the complexity of a motorcycle or television set look paltry in comparison' and describes a small part of what's involved:[12]

> When light first strikes the retina a photon interacts with a molecule called 11-*cis*-retinal, which rearranges within picoseconds to *trans*-retinal. (A picosecond [$10^{-12}$ sec] is about the time it takes light to travel the breadth of a single human hair.) The change in the shape of the retinal molecule forces a change in the shape of the protein, rhodopsin, to which the retinal is tightly bound. The protein's metamorphosis alters its behavior. Now called metarhodopsin II, the protein sticks to another protein, called transducin. Before bumping into metarhodopsin II, transducin had tightly bound a small molecule called GDP. But when transducin interacts with metarhodopsin II, the GDP falls off, and a molecule called GTP binds to transducin. (GTP is closely related to, but different from, GDP.)
>
> GTP-transducin-metarhodopsin II now binds to a protein called phosphodiesterase, located in the inner membrane of the cell. When attached to metarhodopsin II and its entourage, the phosphodiesterase acquires the chemical ability to "cut" a molecule called cGMP (a chemical relative of both GDP and GTP). Initially

---

12.　Behe, M. J., *Darwin's Black Box: The Biochemical Challenge to Evolution*, pp. 46, 18–20, The Free Press, New York, 1996.

there are a lot of cGMP molecules in the cell, but the phosphodiesterase lowers its concentration, just as a pulled plug lowers the water level in a bathtub.

A transparent layer is also far more difficult to obtain than the researchers think. The best explanation for the cornea's transparency is diffraction theory, which shows that light is not scattered if the refractive index doesn't vary over distances more than half the wavelength of light. This in turn requires a certain very finely organized structure of the corneal fibers, which in turn requires complicated chemical pumps to make sure there is exactly the right water content.[13]

Therefore, these simulations do not start from simple beginnings but presuppose vast complexity even to begin with. Also, in their original paper, the researchers admitted 'an eye makes little sense on its own', because the ability to perceive light is meaningless unless the organism has sophisticated computational machinery to make use of this information. For example, it must have the ability to translate 'attenuation of photon intensity' to 'a shadow of a predator is responsible' to 'I must take evasive measures', and be able to act on this information for it to have any selective value. Similarly, the first curving, with its slight ability to detect the direction of light, would only work if the creature had the appropriate 'software' to interpret this. Perceiving actual images is more complicated still. And having the right hardware and software may not be enough—people who have their sight restored after years of blindness take some time to learn to see properly. It should be noted that much information processing occurs in the retina before the signal reaches the brain.

It is also fallacious to point to a series of more complex eyes in nature, and then argue that this presents an evolutionary sequence. This is like arranging a number of different types of aircraft in order of complexity, then claiming that the simple aircraft evolved into complex ones, as opposed to being designed. For one thing, eyes can't descend from other eyes *per se*; rather, organisms pass on genes for eyes to their descendants. This is

13.  Gurney, P.W.V., "Dawkins' Eye Revisited," *JoC* **15**(3):92–99, 2001, creation.com/dawkins-eye-revisted.

important when considering the nautilus eye, a pinhole camera. This cannot possibly be an ancestor of the vertebrate lens/camera eye, because the nautilus as a whole is not an ancestor of the vertebrates, even according to the evolutionists!

## Rotary motors in the bacterial flagellum

*Scientific American* cites another difficult example of irreducible complexity—the rotary motors on bacterial flagellum, but it really has no answers.

### 15. Recent discoveries prove that even at the microscopic level, life has a quality of complexity that could not have come about through evolution.

'Irreducible complexity' is the battle cry of Michael J. Behe of Lehigh University, author of *Darwin's Black Box: The Biochemical Challenge to Evolution*. As a household example of irreducible complexity, Behe chooses the mousetrap—a machine that could not function if any of its pieces were missing and whose pieces have no value except as parts of the whole.

What is true of the mousetrap, he says, is even truer of the bacterial flagellum, a whiplike cellular organelle used for propulsion that operates like an outboard motor. The proteins that make up a flagellum are uncannily arranged into motor components, a universal joint and other structures like those that a human engineer might specify. The possibility that this intricate array could have arisen through evolutionary modification is virtually nil, Behe argues, and that bespeaks intelligent design. [*SA* 84]

Indeed, it does (see diagram, right).

He makes similar points about the blood's clotting mechanism and other molecular systems.

Yet evolutionary biologists have answers to these objections. First, there exist flagellae with forms simpler

Bacterial flagellum with rotary motor, with the following features (after Bacterial Flagella: Paradigm for Design, video, <http://www.arn.org/arnproducts/videos/v021.htm>]:

- Self assembly and repair
- Water-cooled rotary engine
- Proton motive force drive system
- Forward and reverse gears
- Operating speeds of up to 100,000 rpm
- Direction reversing capability within ¼ of a turn
- Hard-wired signal transduction system with short-term memory.

than the one that Behe cites, so it is not necessary for all those components to be present for a flagellum to work. The sophisticated components of this flagellum all have precedents elsewhere in nature, as described by Kenneth R. Miller of Brown University and others. [*SA* 84]

Miller is hardly the epitome of reliability, as shown in Ref. 8. Behe has also responded to critics such as Miller.[14]

In fact, the entire flagellum assembly is extremely similar to an organelle that *Yersinia pestis,* the bubonic plague bacterium, uses to inject toxins into cells. [*SA* 84]

---

14. Behe, M., "Behe responds to various critics," 2000, trueorigin.org/behe08. asp.

This actually comes from the National Center for Science Education's misuses of the research of Dr Scott Minnich, a geneticist and Associate Professor of Microbiology at the University of Idaho. He is a world-class expert on the flagellum who says that belief in design has given him many research insights. His research shows that the flagellum won't form above 37°C, and instead some secretory organelles form from the same set of genes. But this secretory apparatus, as well as the plague bacterium's drilling apparatus, are a *degeneration* from the flagellum, which Minnich says came first although it is more complex.

> The key is that the flagellum's component structures, which Behe suggests have no value apart from their role in propulsion, can serve multiple functions that would have helped favor their evolution. [*SA* 84]

Another problem for this evolutionary 'explanation' is that it is inconsistent with their own theory! Evolution teaches that bacteria evolved before the plants and animals that they could parasitize. So it makes sense that the swimming machinery preceded the secretion machinery that would be needed only once multicellular life evolved. Indeed, evolutionary specialists agree that the flagellum preceded the TTSS:

> It seems plausible that the original type III secretion system for virulence factors evolved from those for flagellar assembly.[15]

We suggest that the flagellar apparatus was the evolutionary precursor of Type III protein secretion systems.[16]

Actually, what Behe says he means by irreducible complexity is that the flagellum could not work without about 40 protein components all organized in the right way. *Scientific American*'s

---

15. Mecsas, J., and Strauss, E.J., "Molecular Mechanisms of Bacterial Virulence: Type III Secretion and Pathogenicity Islands, Emerging Infectious Diseases" **2**(4), October–December 1996; www.cdc.gov/ncidod/EID/vol2no4/mecsas.htm.

16. Nguyen L. *et al.*, "Phylogenetic analyses of the constituents of Type III protein secretion systems," *J. Mol. Microbiol. Biotechnol.* **2**(2):125–44, April 2000.

argument is like claiming that if the components of an electric motor already exist in an electrical shop, they could assemble by themselves into a working motor. However, the right organisation is just as important as the right components.

> The final evolution of the flagellum might then have involved only the novel recombination of sophisticated parts that initially evolved for other purposes. [*SA* 84]

Minnich points out that only about 10 of the 40 components can be explained by co-option, but the other 30 are brand new. Also, the very process of assembly *in the right sequence* requires other regulatory machines, so is in itself irreducibly complex.[17]

## Blood clotting

*Scientific American* cites another serious problem for evolution—blood clotting.

> Similarly, the blood-clotting system seems to involve the modification and elaboration of proteins that were originally used in digestion, according to studies by Russell F. Doolittle of the University of California at San Diego. So some of the complexity that Behe calls proof of intelligent design is not irreducible at all. [*SA* 84]

This is once more a lot of bluff by the atheist Doolittle, or at least poor reading comprehension. He cited recent experiments showing that mice could survive with two of the components of the blood clotting cascade (plasminogen and fibrinogen) eliminated. This supposedly showed that the current cascade was not irreducibly complex but clearly *reducibly* complex. But the experiment *really* showed that the mice lacking both components were better off than one lacking only plasminogen, because the latter suffer from uncleared clots. But the former are hardly as healthy as Doolittle implied, because the only reason they don't suffer from uncleared clots is that they have no functional clotting system at all! A non-functioning clotting system (despite possessing all the many remaining components) is hardly an

---

17. *Unlocking the Mysteries of Life*, video, Illustra Media, 2002.

evolutionary intermediate that natural selection could refine to produce a proper clotting system. Rather, this experiment is evidence against this, because the next step (i.e. from lacking both plasminogen and fibrinogen to fibrinogen only) would be selected *against* because of the uncleared clots.[18]

> Complexity of a different kind—'specified complexity'—is the cornerstone of the intelligent-design arguments of William A. Dembski of Baylor University in his books *The Design Inference* and *No Free Lunch*. Essentially his argument is that living things are complex in a way that undirected, random processes could never produce. The only logical conclusion, Dembski asserts, in an echo of Paley 200 years ago, is that some superhuman intelligence created and shaped life.
>
> Dembski's argument contains several holes. It is wrong to insinuate that the field of explanations consists only of random processes or designing intelligences. Researchers into nonlinear systems and cellular automata at the Santa Fe Institute and elsewhere have demonstrated that simple, undirected processes can yield extraordinarily complex patterns. Some of the complexity seen in organisms may therefore emerge through natural phenomena that we as yet barely understand. But that is far different from saying that the complexity could not have arisen naturally. [SA 84]

Talk about blind faith! But in practice, as Dembski points out, specified complexity in all cases but biology is used as evidence of design, including the search for extraterrestrial intelligence. Since biological complexity is the only exception proposed by evolutionists, it smacks of special pleading.[19]

In addition to the human eye, the flagellum and blood clotting, there's a host of other examples of irreducible complexity in nature. Earlier I alluded to the dynamic sticking mechanism

---

18. For more information, see Behe, M., "In Defense of the Irreducibility of the Blood Clotting Cascade," trueorigin.org/behe03.asp.

19. Grigg, R., "A brief history of design," *Creation* 22(2):50–53, 2000, creation.com/design-history.

in the legs of insects (p. 100). The sticky feet of geckos is another clear example of God's ingenuity[20] with a structure described by its evolutionary discoverers as 'beyond the limits of human technology',[21] along with the lobster eyes with their unique square reflecting geometry that inspired advanced X-ray telescopes and beam producers,[22] the ATP sythase motor (pages 165 ff), etc.

20. Sarfati, J., "Great gecko glue?" *Creation* **23**(1):54–55, 2000, creation.com/gecko.

21. Autumn, K. et al, "Adhesive force of a single gecko foot hair," *Nature* **405**(6787): 681–685, June 8, 2000; perspective by Gee, H., Gripping feat, same issue, p. 631.

22. Sarfati, J., "Lobster eyes brilliant geometric design," *Creation* **23**(3)12–13 2001, creation.com/lobster.

# Chapter 11

# Argument: Evolution of Sex

*Evolutionists say, 'One of the so-called "problems" of evolution—sexuality—can easily be explained.'*

PBS 5 was one of the most revealing about the conflicts between evolution and Christianity. The title is 'Why Sex?' The usual propaganda is that 'science' (stipulatively defined as evolution) is about facts/evidence or 'how' questions, while religion deals with values/faith/morals or 'why' questions. As explained in chapter 2, this is a faulty distinction, and this episode demonstrates this. Here, evolutionary psychology directly affects questions of sexual morality.

The program also spends much time discussing the *advantages* of a fully functional sexual reproductive system, but misleadingly implies that this is sufficient to explain its *origin*.

Sex is said to be more important than life itself, since it enables genes to be passed on to succeeding generations. PBS quotes extensively from Rutgers University evolutionary geneticist Robert Vrijenhoek, who said about sexual reproduction:

> That's our immortality. That's what connects us to humans on into the future. That's what's connected us to all our ancestors in the past. That's what connects us to the ancestors that were fish, the ancestors that were protozoans, and the ancestors that were bacteria. [PBS 5]

Of course the series merely asserted this connection, apart from dubious implications from some common features (see

181

chapter 6). It's also important to note how evolution directly impinges on 'religion' despite the claims that they are compatible (see chapter 2). Vrijenhoek implies that immortality has nothing to do with survival of the individual.

## Asexual *vs* sexual reproduction

The PBS 5 takes its cameras to Texas, where scientists investigated lizards that were entirely female. They laid eggs that hatched into lizards that were clones of the mother. This is called parthenogenesis, from Greek παρθὲνος *parthenos* (virgin) and γὲνεσις *genesis* (birth). They seemed to do very well, so what's the point of sex?

## Disadvantages of sexual reproduction

Indeed, the program acknowledges that sex has many disadvantages, e.g. only 50% of the genes are passed on to an offspring. This means that there is a 50% chance of losing a beneficial mutation. And in a stable population (i.e. not changing the number of individuals), there is on average one surviving offspring per parent, so asexual reproduction is twice as efficient at passing on genes to the next generation. Sex also means that an optimal gene configuration can never be passed on in its entirety.

It is also biologically costly to maintain the sex organs, and to maintain mechanisms to stop the male's immune system destroying his own (genetically different) sperm, and stop the female's immune system destroying incoming sperm or the offspring she carries (in viviparous organisms). And as will be seen in the sexual selection section below, sometimes sexual displays can be cumbersome and make the organism more vulnerable. Females obviously expend a lot of time and energy if they must bear live young. It takes energy to find a mate, otherwise the organism will die without passing on its genes, and if one sex is eliminated, the species will become extinct. It's a lot of trouble, considering that asexual organisms such as bacteria reproduce very quickly.

Because of these hazards, the narrator posed the question, 'Are males really necessary?' Males eat about half the food, and it means that only half the members of the population (females) are involved directly in bearing young. In an asexual population, *all* its members bear offspring directly.

## Advantages of sexual reproduction

Since sexually reproducing species do well, males must have their uses. PBS 5 then shifts to a pool in Sonora, Mexico, inhabited by a species of minnows, both asexually and sexually reproducing ones. But they are infested with a parasite that causes black spot disease. PBS again quotes geneticist Vrijenhoek, says that the sexually reproducing minnows are more resistant than the asexual ones.

The researchers invoked the 'Red Queen Hypothesis', invented by Lee van Valen; Alice (in Wonderland) raced the Red Queen, and exclaimed that they had to keep running just to stay in the same relative position. Evolution is supposed to be a race, and the asexual minnows produced clones, so stopped evolving, so are easy targets. But the sexually reproducing minnows produced lots of variation, so presented a *moving* target. But other evolutionists say: 'The Red Queen idea is simply a cute name for a zoological myth.'[1]

This neat hypothesis seemed to be questioned when a drought eliminated the minnows. When the pool was naturally recolonised, the parasites killed the sexually reproducing ones faster. But it turned out that human-introduced sexually reproducing minnows were still the most resistant of all. The natural colonizers turned out to be inbred, so lost the advantage of variability.

So it seems that the variability is a major advantage, and well worth paying the price of transmitting only 50% of the genes, and the other disadvantages of males. Sexual reproduction also has a 50% chance of losing a harmful mutation without cost to the population (death of an individual).

---

1. Margulis, L. and Sagan, D., *What is sex?* p. 121, Simon and Schuster, NY, 1997.

## Advantage doesn't explain origin!

Creationists can explain the origin of fully functioning sexual reproduction, from the start, in an optimal and genetically diverse population. Once the mechanisms *are already in place*, they have these advantages. But simply having advantages doesn't remotely explain how they could be built from scratch. The hypothetical transitional forms would be highly disadvantageous, so natural selection would work *against* them. In many cases, the male and female genitalia are precisely tuned so one could fit the other, meaning that they could not have evolved independently.

## Evolution of sex?

PBS 5 features a cute cartoon of two single-celled creatures with eyes kissing and exchanging genes. Then the narrator intones:

> Random change produced a creature that was small and fast, which turned out to be an evolutionary advantage. Organisms with reproductive cells like that are called males. Their goal is to find organisms with a different speciality—providing the nutrients life requires. They're called females. These early pioneers evolved into sperm and eggs. [PBS 5]

Hang on—not only is slick animation no substitute for evidence, but somewhere along the line this program jumped from alleged male and female single-celled creatures to multicellular organisms containing cells like them. Then the narrator continued:

> Males produce sperm by the millions—with so many potential offspring, it doesn't pay to be fussy about eggs. A better strategy is to try to fertilize as many eggs as you can. Eggs are more complex than sperm and take a larger investment of energy. Females make a limited number of them. Fewer eggs mean fewer chances to pass on genes, and that means that females—unlike males—do better if they're choosy. At a deep biological level, males and females want different things, regardless of how things appear on

> the surface. ... Small sperm vs large eggs. ... Quantity
> vs quality. [PBS 5]

At about the same time, the program showed a man and woman under a sheet, probably naked but not showing too much of that, indulging in sexual foreplay, then lots of sequences of animals having sex. Is this program really meant for young schoolchildren?

Then the program explains male competition for mates and ornate sexual displays, while females exercise choice. Supposedly the concept of female choice was often discounted in Victorian England (with a female head of state who ruled for more than 60 years).

But the program shifts to a role-reversing bird in Panama. Supposedly the crocodiles ate so many chicks that females leave the males in charge of the eggs while they try to reproduce again. The females are the ones who keep harems, and kill chicks and break eggs of other females. The narrator says:

> So now it's the females who care more about quality than quantity. Now it's the females who fight over mates. Over time, they take on traditionally male characteristics. ... So here is an evolutionary revelation about gender. Male and female roles are not set in stone. They're largely determined by which sex competes for mates, and which invests in the young. [PBS 5]

But before, it was the relative size and speed of sperm and egg that caused males to compete and females to invest more time with their offspring, and other behavioural differences. Now, competition and investment in young are no longer effects but are themselves causes that overturn the roles expected from the differences in gametes. What this really means is that evolution as an explanatory framework is so plastic that its proponents can explain mutually contradictory states of affairs, if they have enough imagination to create plausible just-so stories.

In line with the rest of the series, PBS 5 aims to indoctrinate readers to think that the origin of sex is well explained by evolution.

A decent documentary would not have censored evidence against this view. In reality, evolutionists really have no idea how sex could have evolved. Even the atheist Richard Dawkins says:

> To say, as I have, that good genes can benefit from the existence of sex whereas bad genes can benefit from its absence, is not the same thing as explaining why sex is there at all. There are many theories of why sex exists, and none of them is knock-down convincing. ... Maybe one day I'll summon up the courage to tackle it in full and write a whole book on the origin of sex.[2]

The smug assurances of the PBS program are also contradicted by the evolutionist journal *Science*: "How sex began and why it thrived remain a mystery."[3]

## Sexual selection

Darwin is most famous for the idea that natural selection is a driving force behind evolution. But he realised that this would not explain a number of features that seem to be a hindrance, e.g. the peacock tail. So Darwin invoked the idea of sexual selection, where choice by the opposite sex played a huge part in determining which individuals were able to pass on their genes. Later on, sexual selection is invoked to explain the human brain.

Creationists deny neither natural nor sexual selection. For example, we think it's likely that sexual selection augmented natural selection in producing the different people groups ('races') from a single population of humans that were isolated after Babel.[4]

The difference is that creationists recognize that selection can work only on *existing* genetic information. Evolutionists believe that mutation provides *new* information for selection. But no known mutation has ever increased genetic information, although

2. Dawkins, R., *Climbing Mt Improbable*, p. 75, Penguin Books Ltd. Harmondsworth, Middlesex, England, 1997.

3. Wuethrich, B., "Why sex? Putting the theory to the test," *Science* **281**:1980–1982, 1998.

4. Wieland, C., *One Human Family: The Bible, Science Race and Culture*, Creation Book Publishers, 2011.

there should be many examples observable today if mutation/selection were truly adequate to explain the goo-to-you theory.[5]

## Peacock tail: Darwinian theory fails

Indeed, new research has damaged the sexual selection theory for peacock tails. It turns out that peahens aren't impressed with the peacock's display, and care more for the mating calls. The researchers summarize their seven-year study:

"We found no evidence that peahens expressed any preference for peacocks with more elaborate trains (i.e. trains having more ocelli, a more symmetrical arrangement or a greater length), similar to other studies of galliforms showing that females disregard male plumage. Combined with previous results, our findings indicate that the peacock's train (1) is not the universal target of female choice, (2) shows small variance among males across populations and (3) based on current physiological knowledge, does not appear to reliably reflect the male condition."[6]

A report on this research noted:

> The feather train on male peacocks is among the most striking and beautiful physical attributes in nature, but it fails to excite, much less interest, females, according to new research. The determination throws a wrench in the long-held belief that male peacock feathers evolved in response to female mate choice. It could also indicate that certain other elaborate features in galliformes, a group that includes turkeys, chickens, grouse, quails and pheasants, as well as peacocks, are not necessarily linked to fitness and mating success.[7]

It's not as if the researchers set out to contradict the theory—

5. Note that even if such a mutation were ever discovered, evolutionists would still need to find hundreds more to give their theory the observational boost it desperately needs. See Spetner, L, *Not by Chance*, Judaica Press.

6. Takahashi, M. *et al.*, "Peahens do not prefer peacocks with more elaborate trains," *Anim. Behav.* 2007, doi:10.1016/j.anbehav.2007.10.004.

7. Viegas, J., "Female peacocks not impressed by male feathers," *Discovery News*, March 26, 2008; dsc.discovery.com/news/2008/03/26/peacock-feathers-females.html.

just the opposite in fact—they had planned to *confirm* it. So Charles Darwin's 'theory of sexual selection' *fails to explain the very thing Darwin concocted it for!* [8]

## Chimps and bonobos

The common chimpanzee *Pan troglodytes* and the bonobo (or pygmy chimp) *Pan paniscus* hybridize so are the same biblical kind. Sometimes they are classified as the subspecies *Pan troglodytes troglodytes* and *P. t. paniscus* respectively within the same species. Although they look similar, live in similar environments and eat similar food, their behaviour is different.

Chimps are violent, and bonobos are peaceful. PBS 5 program shows the San Diego Wild Animal Park, and displays bonobos having 'every imaginable' type of recreational copulation, both heterosexual and homosexual, with a running commentary worthy of a hyper-testosteronic adolescent schoolboy.

So how is their behaviour explained? Supposedly by female solidarity: they "can form alliances and cooperatively dominate males" whereas the chimp males abuse females. So how to explain female solidarity? "A relatively simple change in feeding ecology was responsible for this dramatic difference in social behavior." Female bonobos forage on the ground, so have opportunities for social interaction. Female chimps can't do this because gorillas eat the food on the ground, so females must forage on fruit trees alone. Supposedly a drought 2 million years ago killed the gorillas, and enabled a population of chimps to forage on the ground and evolve into bonobos. What a pity, says the program, that we didn't have a similar history and evolve "to be a totally different, more peaceful, less violent, and more sexual species."

As usual, we shouldn't expect actual *evidence* for this story. From the available evidence, it's impossible to prove cause-effect. In other words, how can we disprove that it was the other way round, i.e. that female solidarity didn't generate ground foraging behavior, or even that a gorilla invasion didn't cause bonobos to devolve into chimps?

---

8.    Catchpoole, D., "Peacock tail tale failure," creation.com/tale, 2008.

National Academy of Science fellow Dr Philip Skell (1918–2010), 'The Father of Carbene Chemistry,'[9] noted:

> Further, Darwinian explanations for such things are often too supple: Natural selection makes humans self-centered and aggressive—except when it makes them altruistic and peaceable. Or natural selection produces virile men who eagerly spread their seed—except when it prefers men who are faithful protectors and providers. When an explanation is so supple that it can explain any behavior, it is difficult to test it experimentally, much less use it as a catalyst for scientific discovery.[10]

## Sexual morality *vs* evolutionary psychology

A female may well want the male with the best genes to ensure that her offspring are the 'fittest'. But her best strategy for offspring survival could be finding a male who will stick around and help her care for the young. The male's best strategy is to make sure the offspring are his, so monogamy would have a selective advantage.

But other evolutionary forces threaten monogamy. For example, songbirds are monogamous, but sometimes a female will lust after a male with stronger genes. But this is risky—if the 'husband' finds out, he could kill the offspring.

Concepts from animals are applied to humans in the new field of evolutionary psychology. In the PBS program Geoffrey Miller claimed that our brain is too extravagant to have evolved by natural selection. He claimed, 'It wasn't God, it was our ancestors,' via sexual selection, that shaped our brain 'by choosing their sexual partners for their brains, for their behavior, during courtship.' Art, music and humor played the part of the peacock tail.

---

9.  Skell, P.S. and Woodworth, R.C., "Structure of Carbene $CH_2$," *J. American Chemical Society* **78**(17):4496–4497, 1956 | doi:10.1021/ja01598a087.

10. Skell, P.S., "Why Do We Invoke Darwin? Evolutionary theory contributes little to experimental biology," *The Scientist* 19(16):10, 29 August 2005. Skell wrote a similar article: "The Dangers Of Overselling Evolution: Focusing on Darwin and his theory doesn't further scientific progress," *Forbes* magazine, www.forbes.com, 23 Feb., 2009.

Supposedly this is borne out by tests of human attraction. Men prefer women's faces with full lips, indicating high estrogen; and other facial features, indicating low testosterone. Both are indicators of fertility. So now males do make choices despite having fast and small sperm? Once more, evolution explains *any* state of affairs, so really explains nothing.

Women looking for a short-term fling, or who are ovulating, prefer more masculine faces, indicating 'good' genes. But they prefer more feminine 'gentler' men for a long-term relationship, because they will be more likely to help care for her children. But appearances can be deceptive. We also wonder whether a face of a person from a different people group would be picked as often, although there is no disadvantage to the offspring's genes from so-called inter-racial marriages.[11]

While there's a fleeting disclaimer that evolutionary psychology is controversial even among evolutionists, this program presents Miller's ideas uncritically and unchallenged. But a review of his book *The Mating Mind* in *New Scientist* said:

> How does one actually test these ideas? Without a concerted effort to do this, evolutionary psychology will remain in the realms of armchair entertainment rather than real science.[12]

A leading evolutionary paleoanthropologist, Ian Tattersall, was equally scathing of Miller's book:

> In the end we are looking here at the product of a storyteller's art, not of science.[13]

## Why an episode on sex?

In searching for explanations as to why evolutionists would feel passionately enough about their belief system to spend so many

---

11. Wieland, C., *One Human Family*, Creation Book Publishers, 2011.

12. Birkhead, T., "'Strictly for the birds', review of *The Mating Mind* by Geoffrey Miller," *New Scientist* pp. 48–49, 13 May 2000.

13. Tattersall, I., "'Whatever turns you on', review of *The Mating Mind* by Geoffrey Miller," *New York Times Book Review*, 11 June 2000.

millions foisting it upon the public as in the PBS *Evolution* series, one may not have to look much further than this segment. It is as if those looking for justification of an 'anything goes' approach to sexual morality have had a major hand in this segment. With humans already portrayed as just an advanced species of ape, and sex as a mere tool for propagation of genes, the way the program dwelt on the random hetero/homo 'flings' of our alleged bonobo 'cousins', and the association with an allegedly superior, more peaceful lifestyle, was telling.

# Chapter 12

# Argument: Evolution of Mankind

*Evolutionists say, 'The unique characteristics of the human species can easily be explained.'*

PBS 6—'The Mind's Big Bang'—attempts to explain the biggest difference between humans and animals: our mind, including the advantages of language. However, it makes hardly any attempt to *prove* evolution; rather, it *assumes* it, and makes up stories to explain the differences given this assumption. PBS 1 had already paved the way with misleading arguments about ape-men and DNA similarity.

## Have humans evolved from ape-like creatures?

The similarity between apes and humans is one of the evolutionists' favorite arguments for common descent based on common appearance. The PBS series shouts 'yes' in answer to the question 'have humans evolved from ape-like creatures?', and Episode 1 showed a number of fossils of alleged 'ape-men' for cumulative effect. But this was very deceptive—some of the alleged 'ape-men' they showed are not even accepted by evolutionists as genuine intermediates anymore. For example, it showed an old photograph of Louis Leakey with *Zinjanthropus* (now *Paranthropus*) *boisei* or 'Nutcracker Man', sometimes called a robust australopithecine. But this was long ago relegated to a side branch on man's alleged evolutionary tree.

PBS 1 also claimed that the DNA of chimps and humans was '98%' similar and said the difference between the two species

193

amounts to 'only a couple of spelling errors'. While the 98% is debatable,[1] as is another claim of 99%[2] (it depends on who's telling the story), claiming a 'couple' of differences is outright deception—humans have 3 billion 'letters' (base pairs) of DNA information in each cell, so 2% difference is actually 60 million 'spelling errors'! Of course, this is not 'error' but twenty 500-page books worth of new information that needs to be explained by mutation and selection. Even if we grant 10 million years to the evolutionists, population genetics studies show that animals with human-like generation times of about 20 years could accumulate only about 1700 mutations—not 60 million—in their genome through natural selection in that time frame.[3]

In any case, it seems the importance of DNA similarity in and of itself is overstated; humans and kangaroos share a high degree of genetic similarity, but unlike chimps, they are not supposed to be our close evolutionary relatives.[4]

## Chimp Y chromosome

The human Y chromosome, owned by males, has been recently sequenced, and surprised the evolutionists. The researchers noted the unexpected "extraordinary divergence" from the chimp Y chromosome, including "wholesale renovation".[5] Indeed, the researchers say:

Indeed, at 6 million years of separation, the difference in

1. See also Batten, D., "Human/chimp DNA similarity: Evidence for evolutionary relationship?" *Creation* **19**(1):21–22, 1996, creation.com/human-chimp-dna-similarity; Anderson, D. Decoding the dogma of DNA similarity, 6 June 2007, creation.com/dnadogma; Anderson, D., "Another evolutionary 'truth' now conceded to be a myth," 10 August 2007, creation.com

2. Cohen, C., "Relative Differences: The Myth of 1%," *Science* **316**:1836, 2007.

3. ReMine, W.J., "The Biotic Message: Evolution Versus Message Theory," *Saint Paul Science*, Saint Paul, Minnesota, USA, 1993; see review: Batten, D., *JoC* **11**(3):292–298, 1997; creation.com/biotic.

4. See Wieland, C., "Skippy surprises scientists," 20 January 2009, creation.com/skippy-surprises-scientists.

5. Hughes, J.F. *et al.*, "Chimpanzee and human Y chromosomes are remarkably divergent in structure and gene," *Nature*, advance online publication, 13 January 2010 | doi:10.1038/nature08700content.

MSY [male-specific Y] gene content in chimpanzee and human is more comparable to the difference in autosomal gene content in chicken and human, at 310 million years of separation.

Substituting those changes would be a major problem for evolution.[6,7]

## Missing links found?

Donald Johanson, the discoverer of the alleged missing link 'Lucy', was featured on PBS 2 titled 'Great Transformations'. Supposedly humans are part of evolution, despite our unique abilities to design and create works of art. Allegedly about 7 million years ago, our ancestors swung down from the trees and became bipedal. Then they could gather and carry food, and this food could be higher in energy. This fed bigger brains, which in turn helped food to be gathered more efficiently, in a positive feedback. But Johanson said that there are still differences in the skeletons of chimps and humans, e.g. differently shaped pelvises, different angles where the spine meets the skull, and the way we walk with our knees together while apes walk with their legs far apart.

But PBS offered little actual *evidence*. The fossil record is full of holes, and 'missing link' claims become boring after a while because they are so often discredited.[8] The nearest thing to 'evidence' was Liza Shapiro, University of Texas, showing how flexible the lemur's spine was. The lemur can move on all fours, but leap upright. But this doesn't show how a quadruped can make all the transformations needed to turn it into a proper biped.

*Scientific American* also asserts that we have found a series of hominid fossils that link humans to an ape-like ancestor:

6. Hughes *et al.*, Ref. 5: "We suggest that the extraordinary divergence of the chimpanzee and human MSYs was driven by four synergistic factors: the prominent role of the MSY in sperm production, 'genetic hitchhiking' effects in the absence of meiotic crossing over, frequent ectopic recombination within the MSY, and species differences in mating behaviour."

7. Carter, R.W., "The chimpanzee Y chromosome is radically different from human," creation.com/chimp-y-chromosome, 2 December 2010.

8. E.g. see Sarfati, J., "*Time's* alleged 'ape-man' trips up (again)," *JoC* **15**(3):7–9, 2001, creation.com/kadabba.

... The historical nature of macroevolutionary study involves inference from fossils and DNA rather than direct observation. ... For instance, evolution implies that between the earliest-known ancestors of humans (roughly five million years old) and the appearance of anatomically modern humans (about 100,000 years ago), one should find a succession of hominid creatures with features progressively less ape-like and more modern, which is indeed what the fossil record shows. [*SA* 80]

*Scientific American* also makes this amazing claim:

Perhaps 20 or more hominids (not all of them our ancestors) fill the gap between Lucy the australopithecine and modern humans. [*SA* 83]

The **Power** of **Presuppositions...**

**Three different interpretations of what the fossil *Australopithecus boisei* looked like from the same skull remains.**

**This shows the imagination of scientists and artists. Such "reconstructions" can be made ape-like or human, depending on the artist's viewpoint or belief system.**

How could these alleged '20 or more hominids' fill the gap if they are 'not all our ancestors'? That is, they have fallen out of the gap and into a side alley.

## The 'links' are still missing!

The 'ape-men' fossils are often based on fragmentary remains, and this is true of the latest of a long series of 'missing link claims',

*Ardipithecus ramidus kadabba.*[8] But when more bones are excavated, the specimens are found to be either man or non-man (e.g. australopithecine).

Even if there were such a chain of similar creatures, common appearance does *not* prove common origin. But the claim is groundless, anyway. What the fossil record shows in reality, even granted the evolutionary 'dating' methods, is that this alleged clear-cut progression exists only in the minds of evolutionary popularists. Marvin Lubenow shows that the various alleged 'ape-men' do not form a smooth sequence in evolutionary 'ages', but overlap considerably.[9] For example, the time-span of *Homo sapiens* fossils contains the time-span of the fossils of *Homo erectus*, supposedly our ancestor. Also, when the various fossils are analysed in depth, they turn out not to be transitional or even mosaic. The morphology overlaps too—the analysis of a number of characteristics indicates that *Homo ergaster, H. erectus, H. neanderthalensis* as well as *H. heidelbergensis*, were most likely 'racial' variants of modern man, while *H. habilis* and *H. rudolfensis* were just types of australopithecines.[10] In fact, *H. habilis* is now regarded as an invalid name, probably caused by assigning fragments of australopithecines and *H. erectus* fossils into this 'taxonomic waste bin'.

## Out of Africa?

PBS 6 begins deep in a cave in France, where archaeologist Randy White explores cave paintings, allegedly 30–40 ka (kilo-annum = thousand years ago). The narrator intones about finding out how our ancestors became truly human, and how the mind was born. Then the scene shifts to the Rift Valley in East Africa, where 'humans began'.

Supposedly our branch of the evolutionary tree split off 6 Ma (mega-annum = million years ago) from the line leading to chimps. Our ancestors swung down from the trees and became

---

9.  Lubenow, M., *Bones of Contention*, Baker Books, 1992.

10. Woodmorappe, J., "The non-transitions in 'human evolution'—on evolutionists' terms," *JoC* **13**(2):10–13, 1999, creation.com/non-transitions.

bipedal about 4 Ma, tools were first made 2.5 Ma, early humans began to leave Africa 2 Ma but they would all eventually become extinct, while truly modern humans left Africa 50–60 ka. This is all 'documented' with computer graphics, then by actors.

## Internal evolutionary squabbles overlooked

As shown later, PBS 6 advocates what is called the 'Out of Africa' model, without saying so. This is where modern humans came out of Africa and replaced less evolved hominids that had emerged from Africa much earlier. But there is another evolutionary idea, called the 'multi-regional' or 'regional-continuity' hypothesis, where the hominids that emerged from Africa 2 Ma evolved into modern humans in many parts of the world. This is one of the most vitriolic debates among paleoanthropologists, yet this episode presents only one side. The acrimony between the proponents of these rival theories is due, according to anthropologist Peter Underhill of Stanford University, to: "Egos, egos, egos. Scientists are human." We think *both* sides are right—in their criticisms of each other, because humans did not evolve at all![11]

## Human distinctives

The program showed a skull dated 100 ka, and said that the owner could have been dressed in modern clothes and it would hardly raise an eyebrow. Massachusetts Institute of Technology psychologist Steven Pinker pointed out that modern human babies anywhere in the world can learn any language in the world, and how to count, as well as grow to understand computers. So he suggested: "The distinctively human parts of our intelligence were in place before our ancestors split off into the different continents."

The humans who left Africa 50–60 ka encountered the hominids that had left earlier, that had evolved into Neandertals. They were bigger and stronger than we are, had bigger brains,

11. See Carter, R., "The neutral model of evolution and recent African origins," JoC **23**(1):70–77, 2009, creation.com/african-origins; Anderson, D., "'Out of Africa' theory going out of style?," 2 May 2007, creation.com/out-of-style

and were characterized by having a big nose, receding chin (prognathism) and forehead, almost no cheek, and prominent brow ridges (supraorbital tori).[12] But they were allegedly less creative, with almost no symbolic life or art, and unstructured burial of their dead.[13] Their spear tips were easy to make by chipping stone, but had low range so were used mainly for stabbing. Supposedly they learned by imitation, rather than passing on information via a highly developed language.

The late arrivals, however, had a structured burial of their dead, and made long-range spears with some difficulty by carving antlers for tips. They also invented a spear thrower. Most importantly, they had a sophisticated language that enabled them to transmit information across both distance and time.

They also produced art and culture. PBS 6 demonstrates a 'spit painting' technique they could have used for their cave paintings, and shows that they may have played music by using speleothems (stalactites and stalagmites) as natural percussion instruments.

## Cave men and Neandertals

The publication of the Neandertal genome confirms the biblical creationist belief that the Neandertals were fully human,[14] as do the examples of Neandertal-modern human hybrids. Additionally, various European people groups carry Neandertal genes, indicating at least partial descent from Neandertals.

New discoveries since the first edition of this book support what we said there, because they show that Neandertals were capable of symbolic thought,[15] and even had the leisure time for luxuries like cosmetics.[16] Also, their hands were even more

12. See Wieland, C., "*National Geographic* unveils 'Wilma' the Neandertal lady," 7 October 2000, creation.com/wilma.

13. See Anderson, D., "Putting chimpanzees, 'hominids', and humans in their proper place," 18 July 2007, creation.com/proper-place.

14. See Carter, R., "Neandertal genome like ours," 1 June 2010, creation.com/neandergenes.

15. Sarfati, J., "Neandertals were fully human in their thinking," 30 August 2006, creation.com/neanthought.

16. Carter, R. "The painted Neandertal," 20 May 2010, creation.com/neander-painted.

dexterous than modern humans; giving them the ability to manipulate tools just as effectively, if not more so, than modern humans.[17]

## Cave men and the Bible

One important event recorded in the Bible is the confusion of languages at Babel. The obvious effect was to produce the major language families, from which modern languages have developed. But the division of people according to their newly created language groups had other effects too.

Babel resulted in the isolation of small people groups, each containing a fraction of the total gene pool. This would help fix certain characteristics (called the 'founder effect'). Natural selection and sexual selection would act on these, producing the different people groups ('races') we see today.

Also, some people groups would be isolated from civilization. Consider even the typical small extended family group today, if suddenly isolated from civilization, e.g. on a desert island. Many such groups would not have the ability to smelt metals or build houses. Therefore they would have to use the hardest material available (stone) and make use of already-existing structures (caves). Different family groups would also have different levels of artistic ability. So it shouldn't be too difficult to accept that humans such as *Homo erectus* and Neandertals were probably post-Babel humans who became isolated from major cities, and developed certain physical characteristics because certain genes became fixed due to the small population and selective factors. The notion of a 'stone age' is fallacious—rather, it's a cave/stone technology stage of different people groups. Some people even today have this level of technology, but they live at the same time as us, and are just as human.[18]

---

17. Matthews, M. "Thumbs up for Neandertals," 4 April 2003, creation.com/grip.

18. See Catchpoole, D., "Cave men—in the Bible," *Creation* **23**(3):52–53, 2009, creation.com/bible-cave-men.

## The uniqueness of the human brain

PBS 6 quotes the psychologist Pinker again, who points out that the human brain contains 100 billion cells, and more importantly, it is wired with 100 trillion connections, 'wiring it in precise ways to produce intelligence'. But he attributed this to mutations over tens and hundreds of thousands of years. He has yet to find a single mutation that could increase information, let alone the colossal number required to wire the cerebral supercomputer correctly.

Supposedly this would have been driven by selection for ability to manipulate others. Better language control means better social control.

### *Human v chimp minds*

The PBS episode turns to psychologist Andrew Whiten of the University of St Andrews in Scotland, who tested how young children learned. (Incidentally, on the lintel above the entryway to the school, was the Latin 'In principio erat Verbum', the Vulgate translation of John 1:1, 'In the beginning was the Word'.) He tested children with small models of people, where one 'person' puts an object in one place, goes away, then another 'person' takes this object and hides it somewhere else. Then the first 'person' returns, whereupon the child is asked where he or she would look for the object. A 3-year-old suggests the new hiding place, while a 5-year-old correctly realizes that the first 'person' would have no way of knowing that the object had been moved, and would look in the place he left it. (Sometimes this is called the 'Sally-Anne' test, where the 'Sally' doll hides something in the presence of 'Anne'.) Whiten concluded that by the age of three:

> A child cannot ascribe actions to others. But by the age of five, the child's brain has developed the capacity for stepping into someone else's mind. [PBS 6]

The program contrasts this with chimpanzees, which are incapable of this at any age, "No chimp has passed the test of attribution of false belief."

## Language

There are about 6300 languages in the world today. They all have certain constraints, and obey strict rules, called syntax. This enables us to hierarchically organize information, which is something chimps cannot do, even with the best training in signing.

There is a certain window of opportunity for learning syntax by imitation that gradually closes after the age of seven. PBS 6 shifted to Managua, the capital of Nicaragua, where we meet 'Mary No-name'. She was born deaf, and no one taught her sign language, so she never had a chance to learn syntax. She is still intelligent enough to communicate with some signs, but only to people who know the context.

PBS 6 documents how after the Nicaraguan revolution, US sign language experts tried to teach sign language to deaf people from isolated villages, but failed. But the children developed their own sign language instead, which is a real language with proper syntax and as much capacity for expressing complex thought as spoken language. They wanted to communicate with other people like themselves rather than have a language imposed upon them.

Deaf people actually process sign language with the same areas of the brain that hearing people use to process spoken language, including Broca's area and Wernicke's area. This is shown by deaf patients who have damage to either area, who have an equivalent type of aphasia (language impairment) in sign language to that a hearing person would suffer in spoken language.[19]

## Evolution of language?

None of the above has anything to do with evolution. The language processing areas are unique to humans, and enable us to use syntax in both written and sign language.

All the same, atheist Richard Dawkins of Oxford University presents his usual storytelling on PBS 6 about how language conferred a selective advantage, so left more offspring. It's

---

19. Hickok, G., Bellugi, U., Klima, E.S., "Sign language in the brain," *Scientific American* **284**(6):42–49, June 2001.

interesting that the only topic this well-known propagandist for neo-Darwinism is interviewed on is language, although Dawkins' field is biology, not linguistics. It's also notable that the PBS series did not show Dawkins promoting his rabid atheistic religion (as exemplified in his book *The God Delusion*[20] (2006)), which he makes plain is a main reason for his promotion of Darwin. Presumably the producers didn't want to make the materialistic implications of evolution *too* obvious to an American public that might still be repulsed by overt atheism.

PBS 6 explains how Robin Dunbar of Liverpool University has researched the way people use language, and he rejects the idea that the main function is to exchange information. Rather, about two-thirds is social interactions, what he called 'gossip'. So natural selection favored those with the most refined social skills, which would have the advantages of holding big groups together and being able to find out information about third parties.

## Difficulties with language evolution

It's one thing to claim that languages evolved, but it's another to provide a mechanism. Evolutionists usually claim that languages evolved from animal grunts. Some even claim that the continuing change of languages is just like biological evolution. However, actual observations of language present a very different picture.

First, ancient languages were actually extremely complex with many different inflections. There is no hint of any build-up from simpler languages. For example, in the Indo-European family, Sanskrit, Classical Greek and Latin had many different noun inflections for different case, gender and number, while verbs were inflected for tense, voice, number and person. Modern descendants of these languages have greatly *reduced* the number of inflections, i.e. the trend is from complex to simpler, the *opposite* of evolution. English has almost completely lost inflections, retaining just a few like the possessive "–'s".

English has also lost 65–85% of the Old English vocabulary, and many Classical Latin words have also been lost from its descendants,

20. See Bell, P., "Atheist with a Mission: Critique of *The God Delusion* by Richard Dawkins," *JoC* 21(2):28–34, 2007; creation.com/delusion.

the Romance languages (Spanish, French, Italian, etc.).

Second, most of the changes were *not* random, but the result of *intelligence*. For example: forming compound words by joining simple words and derivations, by adding prefixes and suffixes, by modification of meaning, and by borrowing words from other languages including calques (a borrowed compound word where each component is translated and then joined). There are also unconscious, but definitely non-random, changes such as systematic sound shifts, for example those described by Grimm's Law (which relates many Germanic words to Latin and Greek words).[21]

## Memes

Dawkins said on PBS 6, 'The Mind's Big Bang':

> The only kind of evolutionary change we're likely to see very much of is not genetic information at all, it's cultural evolution. And if we put a Darwinian spin on that, then we're going to be talking about the differential survival of memes, as opposed to genes. [PBS 6]

Dawkins proposed the meme idea long ago in his book *The Selfish Gene*, and psychologist Sue Blackmore of the University of West of England has been one of his recent champions. She said on PBS 6:

> Memes are ideas, habits, skills, gestures, stories, songs—anything which we pass from person to person by imitation. We copy them. ... just as the competition between genes shapes all of biological evolution, so it's the competition between memes that shapes our minds and cultures.
>
> ... Nowadays I would say that memetic evolution is going faster and faster, and it has almost entirely taken over from biological evolution. ...

21. May, K., Talking Point, *Creation* 23(2):42–45, 2001, creation.com/talking-point; Steel, A., "The development of languages is nothing like biological evolution," *JoC* **14**(2):31–40, 2000, creation.com/language_development; Field, F. "The language faculty: following the evidence," *JoC* **22**(1):73–80, 2008, creation.com/language.

> The more educated you are, the less children you
> have. That is memes fighting against genes. [PBS 6]

Now memes have apparently found a new home, the Internet, and it has actually enslaved us, we are told.

Blackmore even believes that the idea of the 'self' is an illusion produced by competing memes in the brain. But under her own system, we must ask her, "Who is (or rather, what are) actually proposing this idea?"!

But it becomes ridiculous when things such as the Internet, birth control, any invention, insulin, are called 'memes'. A term that describes everything really describes nothing. All that she's done is to apply the same label to just about anything, but this adds nothing to our knowledge.

It's no wonder that the evolutionist, Jerry Coyne, called Blackmore's book "a work not of science, but of extreme advocacy." He says that memes are "but a flashy new wrapping around a parcel of old and conventional ideas." Coyne also believes that evolutionary psychology is non-science (and nonsense). Coyne is no creationist sympathizer but an ardent—but ineffective—opponent of creation.[22]

The Discovery Institute critique of the PBS series points out that, if the likes of Eugenie Scott were truly concerned about non-science being taught in the science classroom, she would oppose evolutionary psychology and memetic evolution as well, and certainly not support using this PBS series in science classrooms. No, what she's opposed to is challenges to her materialistic faith.

## Conclusion

From all the money and time lavished on the PBS *Evolution* series, major articles in science journals, and political campaigns to keep teachers from presenting alternatives to evolution in schools, it is evident that the evolutionists fear the increasing spread of creationist information, despite their best efforts at

---

22. See Wieland, C., "New eyes for blind cave fish?" creation.com/cave_fish, 9 August 2000. Sarfati, J., "Christopher Hitchens—blind to salamander reality," creation.com/hitchens, 26 July 2008.

censorship. So they are desperate to counteract this information. But their efforts don't withstand scientific scrutiny, and in the end any reasonable observer would have to admit that evolution is a deduction from a materialistic belief system. It is philosophy/religion dressed up as 'science'.

# Appendix 1:

## Common Arguments for Evolution That Have Been Rejected

This book has been organized around the most powerful arguments that evolutionists can muster (quoting the salient points of PBS and *Scientific American*) against the best arguments of creationists. Too often, both sides get sidetracked on bad arguments. We believe that all Bible-believers should have solid answers about the real issues of the debate (e.g., two worldviews are in conflict; we disagree about interpretation, not the facts themselves).

This doesn't mean that Christians should ignore the weak arguments or the potshots. We have added an appendix to address some of these arguments.

### Rejected argument 1: Similarities between embryos[1]

Most people have heard that the human embryo goes through various evolutionary stages, such as having gill slits like a fish, a tail like a monkey, etc. This concept, pretentiously called the 'biogenetic law,' was popularized by the German evolutionist Ernst Haeckel in the late 1860s. It is also known as 'embryonic recapitulation' or 'ontogeny recapitulates phylogeny,' meaning that during an organism's early development it supposedly retraces its evolutionary history.

Although this idea was based on a fraud and has been debunked by many high-profile scientists, the idea persists.

---

1.  Adapted with permission from chapter 7, Batten, D. ed. *et al.*, *The Creation Answers Book*, Creation Book Publishers, Brisbane, Australia, 2006.

**Top row:** Haeckel's drawings of several different embryos, showing incredible similarity in their early 'tailbud' stage.

**Bottom row:** Richardson's photographs of how the embryos really look at the same stage of development.

Even textbooks in the new millennium were still using Haeckel's fraudulent drawings.[2]

## Haeckel's fraud exposed

Within months of the publication of Haeckel's work in 1868, L. Rütimeyer, professor of zoology and comparative anatomy at the University of Basel, showed it to be fraudulent. William His Sr, professor of anatomy at the University of Leipzig, and a famous comparative embryologist, corroborated Rütimeyer's criticisms.[3] These scientists showed that Haeckel fraudulently modified his drawings of embryos to make them look more alike. Haeckel even reprinted some woodcuts and then claimed they were embryos of different species!

Has the 'biogenetic law' any merit? In 1965, evolutionist George Gaylord Simpson said, 'It is now firmly established that ontogeny does not repeat phylogeny.'[4] Prof. Keith Thompson (biology, Yale) said:

2.  Even in the 21st century, we find colourized versions of Haeckel's embryo drawings, for example, in Mader, S. S. *Biology,* p. 278, 10th Edition, McGraw Hill, 2010. These sketches of Haeckel are often wrongly ascribed to Romanes, 1901.

3.  Rusch, W.H. Sr., "Ontogeny Recapitulates Phylogeny," *Creation Research Society Quarterly* **6**(1):27–34, 1969.

4.  Simpson and Beck, *An Introduction to Biology*, p. 241, 1965.

Surely the biogenetic law is as dead as a doornail. It was finally exorcised from biology textbooks in the fifties. As a topic of serious theoretical inquiry, it was extinct in the twenties.[5]

Despite the evidence of fraud, Haeckel's drawings are still widely believed to bear some resemblance to reality. But an investigation published in 1997 has revealed that Haeckel's fraud was far worse than anyone realized. An embryologist, Dr Michael Richardson, with the co-operation of biologists around the world, collected and photographed the types of embryos Haeckel supposedly drew.[6] Dr Richardson found that Haeckel's drawings bore little resemblance to the embryos.[7] *The Times* (London) quotes Richardson:

This is one of the worst cases of scientific fraud. It's shocking to find that somebody one thought was a great scientist was deliberately misleading. It makes me angry. What he [Haeckel] did was to take a human embryo and copy it, pretending that the salamander and the pig and all the others looked the same at the same stage of development. They don't. These are fakes.[8]

A human embryo never looks reptilian or pig-like. A human embryo is always a human embryo, from the moment of conception; it is never anything else. It does not *become* human sometime after eight weeks. This is what the Bible says—the unborn baby is a tiny human child (Gen. 25:21–22, Ps. 139:13–16, Jer. 1:5, Luke 1:41–44).

---

5. Thompson, K., "Ontogeny and Phylogeny Recapitulated," *American Scientist* **76**:273, 1988

6. The embryo photos used in this article were kindly supplied by Dr Michael K. Richardson. They originally appeared in M.K. Richardson *et al.*, ©Springer-Verlag GmbH & Co., Tiergartenstrasse, 69121 Heidelberg, Germany, 1997. "There is no highly conserved stage in the vertebrates: implications for current theories of evolution and development," *Anatomy and Embryology* **196**(2):91–106.

7. Van Niekerk, E., "Countering revisionism—part 1: Ernst Haeckel, fraud *is* proven," *JoC* **25**(3):89–95, 2011; "Part 2, Ernst Haeckel and his triple-woodcut print," *JoC* **27**(1):78–84, 2013.

8. Hawkes, N. *The Times* (London), 11 August 1997, p. 14.

## *Some similarities in early embryos are inevitable*

Admittedly, the embryos of animals bear *some* resemblance in their early stages of development, but not in the way that evolutionists usually portray it. But this makes perfect sense from a design standpoint. To construct anything, you begin with something without shape, or with a basic form, and then you add increasingly specialized details.

An illustration from pottery may help. A potter starts with a lump of clay. Whether he wants to make a goblet or a slender vase, the potter shapes the clay initially into a cylinder. At this stage both the goblet and the vase look similar—they have the same basic plan. Further work results in the goblet and vase looking more and more different. (The analogy with embryos breaks down in that the potter could change his mind and make *either* a vase or goblet at the completion of the basic plan. A fish embryo, however, could never become a human embryo [or vice versa] because a fish embryo has the coded instructions in the DNA only for making a fish.)

Some principles known as von Baer's laws express this concept in regard to embryo development. Namely, the general features of animals appear earlier in the embryo's development than the specialized features. Each embryo of a given species, instead of passing through the stages of other animals (in either adult or embryonic form), departs more and more from general features as it develops.

Von Baer's laws indicate that the younger the embryonic stage, the more closely organisms tend to resemble each other.

## Rejected argument 2: Peppered moths

The 'textbook story' of England's famous peppered moths (*Biston betularia*) goes like this. The moth comes in light and dark (melanic) forms. Pollution from the Industrial Revolution darkened the tree trunks, mostly by killing the light-colored covering lichen (plus soot).

The lighter forms, which had been well camouflaged against the light background, now 'stood out,' and so birds more readily ate them. Therefore, the proportion of dark moths increased dramatically. Later, as pollution was cleaned up, the light moth became predominant again.

The shift in moth numbers was carefully documented through catching them in traps. Release-recapture experiments confirmed that in polluted forests, more of the dark form survived for recapture, and *vice versa*. In addition, birds were filmed preferentially eating the less camouflaged moths off tree trunks.[9,10,11]

The story has generated boundless evolutionary enthusiasm. H.B. Kettlewell, who performed most of the classic experiments, said that if Darwin had seen this, 'He would have witnessed the consummation and confirmation of his life's work.'[12]

Actually, even as it stands, the textbook story demonstrates nothing more than gene frequencies shifting back and forth, by natural selection, within one created kind. It offers nothing which, even given millions of years, could add the sort of complex design information needed for amoeba-to-man evolution.

Even L. Harrison Matthews, a biologist so distinguished he was asked to write the foreword for the 1971 edition of Darwin's *Origin of Species*, said therein that the peppered moth example showed natural selection, but *not* 'evolution in action.'

However, it turns out that this classic story is full of holes anyway. *Peppered moths don't even rest on tree trunks during the day.*

Kettlewell and others attracted the moths into traps in the forest either with light, or by releasing female pheromones—in each case, they only flew in *at night*. So where do they spend the day? British scientist Cyril Clarke, who investigated the peppered moth extensively, wrote:

But the problem is that we do not know the resting

9.  Wieland, C., "Goodbye, peppered moths," *Creation* **21**(3):56, 1999, creation.com/peppered.

10. Wieland, C., "The Moth Files: An update on the Peppered Moth fiasco," *Creation* **25**(1):14–15, 2002, creation.com/moth.

11. Wieland, C., "More about moths: A recent attempt to restore the reputation of the peppered moth as an evolutionary icon falls flat," creation.com/moths, 5 January 2008.

12. Kettlewell, H.B., "Darwin's missing evidence, Evolution and the Fossil Record," p. 23, *Readings from Scientific American*, W.H. Freeman and Co., San Francisco, CA, 1978.

sites of the moth during the day time ... . In 25 years we have found only two *betularia* on the tree trunks or walls adjacent to our traps (one on an appropriate background and one not), and none elsewhere.[13]

The moths filmed being eaten by the birds were laboratory-bred ones placed onto tree trunks by Kettlewell; they were so languid that he once had to warm them up on his car hood.[14]

And all those still photos of moths on tree trunks? One paper described how it was done—*dead moths were glued to the tree*.[15] University of Massachusetts biologist Theodore Sargent helped glue moths onto trees for a NOVA documentary. He says textbooks and films have featured "a lot of fraudulent photographs."[16]

Other studies have shown a very poor correlation between the lichen covering and the respective moth populations. And when one group of researchers glued dead moths onto trunks in an unpolluted forest, the birds took more of the dark (less camouflaged) ones, as expected. But their traps captured *four times as many dark moths as light ones*—the opposite of textbook predictions![17]

The University of Chicago's Jerry Coyne said that such painful revelations about the moth story ('the prize horse in our stable') was like finding out that Santa Claus was not real. Quoted by creationists, he now insists the peppered moths do somehow demonstrate 'evolution' after all.

Regrettably, hundreds of millions of students have once more been indoctrinated with a 'proof' of evolution which is riddled with error, fraud and half-truths.[18]

---

13. Clarke, C.A., Mani, G.S., and Wynne, G., "Evolution in reverse: Clean air and the peppered moth," *Biological Journal of the Linnean Society* **26**:189–199, 1987, p. 197.

14. *Calgary Herald*, 21 March 1999, p. D3.

15. Lees, D.R., Creed, E.R., "Industrial melanism in Biston betularia: the role of selective predation," *Journal of Animal Ecology* **44**:67–83, 1975.

16. Coyne, J.A., *Nature* **396**(6706):35–36; *The Washington Times*, p. D8, 17 January 1999.

17. Lees, D.R., Creed, E.R., "Industrial melanism in Biston betularia: the role of selective predation," *Journal of Animal Ecology* **44**:67–83, 1975.

18. Unfettered by evolutionary 'just so' stories, researchers can now look

## Rejected argument 3: Vestigial organs

Evolutionists often argue that such things as flightless birds' small wings, pigs' toes, male nipples, legless lizards, the rabbit's digestive system, the human appendix, and hip bones and teeth in whales are useless and have no function. They claim these features are 'leftovers of evolution' and evidence for evolution.

The 'vestigial' organ argument for evolution is an old chestnut, but it is not valid.

First, it is impossible to prove that an organ is useless. The function may simply be unknown and its use may be discovered in the future. This has happened with more than 100 formerly alleged useless vestigial organs in humans that are now known to be essential.

Second, even if the alleged vestigial organ were no longer needed, it would prove 'devolution' not evolution. The creation model allows for deterioration of a perfect creation since the Fall. However, the particles-to-people evolution model needs to find examples of *nascent* organs, i.e., those which are *increasing* in complexity.

### Wings on birds that do not fly?

There are at least two possibilities as to why flightless birds such as ostriches and emus have wings:

1. The wings are indeed 'useless' and derived from birds that once could fly. This is possible in the creationist model. Loss of features is relatively easy by natural processes, whereas acquisition of new characters, requiring specific new DNA information, is impossible. Loss of wings most probably occurred in a beetle species that colonized a windy island. Again, this is *loss* of genetic information, so

---

for the real causes of these population shifts. Might the dark form actually have a function, like absorbing more warmth? Could it reflect conditions in the caterpillar stage? In a different nocturnal moth species, Sargent has found that the plants eaten by the larvae may induce or repress the expression of such melanism in adult moths (see Sargent, T.R. et al. in Hecht, M.K. *et al.*, *Evolutionary Biology*, Plenum Press: New York, NY, 1998.

it is not evidence for microbe-to-man evolution, which requires masses of new genetic information.[19]

2.  The wings have a function. Some possible functions, depending on the species of flightless bird, are: balance while running, cooling in hot weather, warmth in cold weather, protection of the rib cage in falls, mating rituals, scaring predators (emus will run at perceived enemies of their chicks, mouth open and wings flapping), sheltering of chicks, etc. If the wings are useless, why are the muscles functional, allowing these birds to move their wings?

## Pigs with two toes that do not reach the ground?

Does this mean that the shorter toes have no function? Not at all. Pigs spend a lot of time in water and muddy conditions for cooling purposes. The extra toes probably make it easier to walk in mud (a bit like the rider wheels on some long trucks that only touch the road when the truck is heavily loaded). Perhaps the muscles attached to the extra toes give strength to the 'ankle' of the pig.

## Why do males have nipples?

Males have nipples because of the common plan followed during early embryo development. Embryos start out producing features common to male and female—again an example of 'design economy'. Nipples are a part of this design economy. However, as Bergman and Howe point out, the claim that they are useless is debatable.[20]

What is the evolutionist's explanation for male nipples? Did males evolve (devolve) from females? Or did ancestral males suckle the young? No evolutionist would propose this. Male nipples are neither evidence for evolution nor evidence against creation.

19.  Wieland, C., "Beetle bloopers," *Creation* **19**(3):30, 1997, creation.com/beetle-bloopers.

20.  Bergman, J., Howe, G., "'Vestigial organs' are fully functional," *Creation Research Society Monograph No. 4*, Creation Research Society Books: Terre Haute, IN, 1990.

## Why do rabbits have digestive systems that function 'so poorly that they must eat their own feces'?

This is an incredible proposition. One of the most successful species on earth would have to be the rabbit! The rabbit's mode of existence is obviously very efficient (what about the saying 'to breed like rabbits'?) Just because eating feces may be abhorrent to humans, it does not mean it is inefficient for the rabbit. Rabbits have a special pouch called the *caecum*, containing bacteria, at the beginning of the large intestine. These bacteria aid digestion, just as bacteria in the rumen of cattle and sheep aid digestion. Indeed, rabbits 'chew the cud' in a manner that parallels sheep and cattle.

The rabbit produces two types of fecal pellet—a hard one and a special soft one coming from the caecum. It is only the latter that is eaten to enrich the diet with the nutrients produced by the bacteria in the caecum. In other words, this ability of rabbits is a design feature; it is not something they have learned to do because they have 'digestive systems that function so poorly.' It is part of the variety of design, which speaks of creation, not evolution.

Skeptics have claimed the Bible is in error in saying that the rabbit 'chews the cud' (Lev. 11:6). The Hebrew literally reads, 'raises up what has been swallowed.' The rabbit *does* re-eat what has been swallowed—its partly digested fecal pellets. The skeptics are wrong again.

### Legless lizards

It is quite likely that legless lizards could have arisen through loss of genetic information from an original created kind, and the structures are consistent with this. 'Loss' of a structure is of no comfort to evolutionists, as they have to find a mechanism for creating new structures, not losing them. Loss of information cannot explain how evolution 'from amoeba to man' could occur. Genesis 3:14 suggests that snakes may have once had legs.[21]

Adaptation and natural selection are biological facts;

---

21. Brown, C., "The origin of the snake (letter)," *Creation Research Society Quarterly* **26**:54, 1989, Brown suggests that monitor lizards may have been the precursors of snakes.

amoeba-to-man evolution is not. Natural selection can only work on the genetic information present in a population of organisms—it cannot create new information. For example, since no known reptiles have genes for feathers, no amount of selection will produce a feathered reptile. Mutations in genes can only modify or eliminate existing structures, not create new ones. If in a certain environment a lizard survives better with smaller legs, or no legs, then varieties with this trait will be selected for. This might more accurately be called *devolution*, not evolution.

Rapid minor changes in limb length can occur in lizards, as demonstrated on Bahamian islands by Losos and others.[22] The changes occurred much faster than evolutionists thought they could. Such changes do not involve new genetic information and so give no support to microbe-to-man evolution. They do illustrate how quickly animals could have adapted to different environments after the Flood.

## The human appendix

It is now known that the human appendix contains lymphatic tissue and helps control bacteria entering the intestines. It functions in a similar way to the tonsils at the upper end of the alimentary canal, which are known to fight throat infections. They also provide a safe house for beneficial bacteria, so they can repopulate the large intestine after a dystentery attack flushes out all bacteria.[23] Tonsils also were once thought to be useless organs.

## Hip bones in whales

Some evolutionists claim that these bones show that whales evolved from land animals. However, Bergman and Howe point

22. Losos, J.B., Warheit, K.I., Schoener, T.W., "Adaptive differentiation following experimental island colonization in Anolis lizards," *Nature* **387**:70–73, 1997. See comment by Case, T.J., *Nature* 387:15–16; "Fast lizard changes delight creationists," *Creation* **19**(4):9, 1997, creation.com/focus-194.

23. See Wieland, C., Doyle, S., "More musings on our 'useless' appendix," 6 August 2008, creation.com/appendix4.

out that they are different in male and female whales. They are not useless at all, but help with reproduction (copulation).[24]

## Teeth in embryonic baleen whales

Evolutionists claim that these teeth show that baleen whales evolved from toothed whales. However, they have not provided an adequate mechanism for scrapping one perfectly good system (teeth) and replacing it with a very different system (baleen or whalebone). Also, the teeth in the embryo function as guides for the correct formation of the massive jaws.

As Scadding, an evolutionist, said, "… vestigial organs provide no evidence for evolutionary theory."[25]

---

24. See Wieland, C., "The strange tale of the leg on the whale," *Creation* **20**(3):10–13, 1998, creation.com/whaleleg.

25. Scadding, S.R., "Do vestigial organs provide evidence for evolution?," *Evolutionary Theory* **5**:173–176, 1981.

# Appendix 2

## Common Arguments for Creation that Should Not Be Used

T here are many strong arguments for creation, but some are not so strong, and others are totally unsound.[1] It's important to know the difference. This is why it's important to keep up with current creationist literature. There is so much good evidence for creation that there is no need to use any of the 'doubtful' arguments. Using discredited arguments rebounds on the user, and it's a poor testimony for the cause of Christ. It's the *truth* that sets us free (John 8:32), not error—and Christ is "the truth" (John 14:6)!

Christians should not become alarmed when they find out creationist researchers have overturned their favourite arguments. Rather, they should refocus on the main issue, the authority of the Word of God, the 66 books of the Bible,[2] not the theories of fallible humans, whether creationist or evolutionist.

### Our starting point

The authority of the Bible is the main emphasis of Creation Ministries International. We don't try to 'prove' the Bible with science; rather, we accept the Bible's propositions as true without proof, i.e., as *axioms* or *presuppositions*.

*All* philosophical systems, not just Christianity, start with axioms. There are good reasons for accepting the axioms of Scripture as true, because it can be shown that they lead to a

---

1. Based on Sarfati, J., "Moving forward: arguments we think creationists shouldn't use," *Creation* **24**(2):20–34, 2002, creation.com/moving-forward.

2. See Sarfati, J., "The authority of Scripture," *Apologia* **3**(2):12–16, 1994, reprinted at creation.com/authority.

consistent view of physical and moral reality, which other axioms can't provide.

Genesis contains a number of Hebrew grammatical features that show it was intended to teach a straightforward history of the world from its creation. Genesis, backed up by the rest of Scripture, unambiguously teaches that:

- The heavens, earth, and everything in them were created in six consecutive normal days, the same as those of our work week (Exod. 20:8–11).

- Earth is about 6,000 years old, since Jesus said mankind was there "from the beginning of creation," not billions of years later (Mark 10:6).

- Adam sinned and brought physical death to mankind (Rom. 5:12–19; 1 Cor. 15:21–22).

- Since man was the federal head of creation, the whole creation was cursed (Rom 8:20–22), which included death to animals, with the end of the original vegetarian diet for both humans and animals (Gen. 1:29–30).

- God judged the world by a globe-covering flood, which Jesus and Peter compared with the coming Judgment (Luke 17:26–27; 2 Peter 3:3–7). This destroyed all land vertebrate animals and people not on the ocean-liner-sized ark.

- God then judged the people by confusing their language at Babel—after they refused to spread out and repopulate the earth after the Flood.

## Using this Framework

It's important to realize that all "facts" of science do *not* speak for themselves, but are *interpreted* within a framework. Evolutionists start with the axiom of *naturalism* or *materialism*, i.e., God (if He even exists) performed no miraculous acts of creation.

Biblical creationists interpret the *same* facts and observations, but within the framework outlined above.

## What should we defend, and what should we hold loosely?

It's very important to distinguish the biblical framework from various creationist scientific models within this framework. To Christians, the *framework* should be non-negotiable, but the *models* should never be held dogmatically.

All theories of science are fallible, and new data often overturn previously held theories. Evolutionists continually revise their theories because of new data, so it should not be surprising or distressing that some creationist scientific theories need to be revised, too.

CMI has never promoted many of the fallacious creationist arguments listed here. Indeed, some have not been promoted by *any* major creationist organization; rather, they are straw men set up by anti-creationists. [3]

Ironically, some skeptics criticize creationists when they retract doubtful arguments, but the same people accuse creationists of being unwilling to change their minds.

## Which arguments should definitely not be used? [4]

### 'Darwin recanted on his deathbed'.

Many people use this story, originally from a Lady Hope. However, it is almost certainly not true, and there is no corroboration from those who were closest to him, even from Darwin's wife Emma, who never liked evolutionary ideas. Also, even if true, so what? If a prominent creationist recanted

The real "Lady Hope" of the "Darwin recanted" legend was buried in this grave located at the Rookwood Cemetery in Sydney, Australia.

---

3.   Those (such as Hugh Ross) who believe that God created over billions of years, and thus have death occurring before sin, are also guilty of building straw men. See, for instance, Sarfati, J., "Trilobites on the ark?," 30 July 2004, creation.com/trilobites.

4.   For an exhaustive, updated list, see creation.com/dont_use.

Creation, would that disprove it? There is no value to this argument whatever.[5]

### 'Moon-Dust thickness proves a young moon.'

For a long time, creationists claimed that the dust layer on the moon was too thin if dust had truly been falling on it for billions of years. They based this claim on early estimates—by evolutionists—of the influx of moon dust, and worries that the moon landers would sink into this dust layer. But these early estimates were wrong, and by the time of the Apollo landings, NASA was not worried about sinking. So the dust layer thickness can't be used as proof of a young moon (or of an old one either).[6]

### 'NASA computers, in calculating the positions of planets, found a missing day and 40 minutes, proving Joshua's "long day" and Hezekiah's sundial movement of Joshua 10 and 2 Kings 20.'

Not promoted by major creationist organizations, but an hoax in wide circulation, especially on the Internet.

Essentially the same story, now widely circulated on the Internet, appeared in the somewhat unreliable 1936 book *The Harmony of Science and Scripture* by Harry Rimmer. Evidently an unknown person embellished it with modern organization names and modern calculating devices.

Also, the whole story is mathematically impossible—it requires a *fixed reference point* before Joshua's long day. In fact we would need to cross-check between *both* astronomical *and* historical records to detect any missing day. And to detect a missing 40 minutes requires that these reference points be known to within an accuracy of a few minutes. It is certainly true that the timing of solar eclipses observable from a certain location can be known precisely. But the ancient records did not record time that precisely, so the required cross-check is simply not possible.

---

5.  Grigg, R., "Did Darwin recant?," *Creation* **18**(1):36–37, 1995, creation.com/recant.

6.  See Snelling, A., Rush, D., "Moon dust and the age of the solar system," *JoC* **7**(1):2–42, 1993, creation.com/moondust.

Anyway, the earliest historically recorded eclipse occurred in 1217 BC, nearly two centuries after Joshua. So there is no way the missing day could be detected by any computer.[7]

Note that discrediting this myth doesn't mean that the events of Joshua 10 didn't happen. Features in the account support its reliability, e.g. the moon was also slowed down. This was not necessary to prolong the day, but this would be observed from Earth's reference frame if God had accomplished this miracle by slowing Earth's rotation.[8]

## 'Woolly mammoths were snap frozen during the Flood catastrophe.'

This is contradicted by the geological setting in which mammoths are found. It's most likely that they perished toward the end of the Ice Age, possibly in catastrophic dust storms. Partially digested stomach contents are not proof of a snap freeze, because the elephant's stomach functions as a holding area—a mastodon with preserved stomach contents was found in mid-western USA, where the ground was not frozen.[9]

## 'NASA faked the moon landings.'

This NASA hoax claim is an example of where CMI reminds readers that we are pro-Bible rather than anti-establishment for the sake of it.

First, it is biblical to trust multiple eye-witnesses (cf. Deuteronomy 19:15), and one impeccable witness is the late

7.   See Thompson, B., "Has NASA discovered a 'missing day'?," *Reason & Revelation* 11(5):17–19, May 1991, reprinted at creation.com/nasa.

8.   See Grigg, R., "Joshua's long day," *Creation* 19(3):35–37, 1997, creation.com/longday.

9.   Oard, M., "The extinction of the woolly mammoth," *JoC* 14(3):24–34, 2000, creation.com/snapfreeze.

James Irwin, who was a staunch biblical creationist and walked on the moon. Also, Australia must have been in on the alleged hoax; the huge radio antenna at Parkes Observatory, New South Wales, was used to relay the signals from the moon, since it was on the Australian not the American side of Earth (cf. the Australian film *The Dish*, 2000). We can also shine powerful lasers to *certain* spots on the moon and detect reflected light of the laser frequency, possible only if someone had been to the moon and *laid out retro-reflectors in those spots.*[10]

Second: the hoax claims show faulty understanding of science (cf. *Mythbusters* episode **#104** (0702), 2008):

CLAIM: Photos should show parallel shadows with only one light source, the sun; non-parallel shadows prove it was a studio set with multiple lights. *Actually, because of the irregular lunar topography, parallel shadows can* **look** *non-parallel in the perspective of the film.*

CLAIM: Astronaut in the shadow of the spacecraft was easily visible, which would not have been possible with only one light source. *This forgets another source:* **moonlight***! Reflected light from the lunar surface would make the astronaut easily visible. Also, Earthlight is much brighter on the moon than moonlight is on earth, because Earth is much higher in both surface area and albedo.*

CLAIM: Photos had no stars, hence they were in a studio. *No, a camera set for optimal performance in the bright light of the lunar surface would not be sensitive enough to show stars.*

CLAIM: Footprints would not have been left in sand without moisture to hold the sand in place. *True on* **earth***, where water tends to round out sand grains. The lunar grains were angular and held the shape.*

CLAIM: The flag fluttered, so there must have been a breeze. *No, the astronaut twisted the flagpole to plant it in the moon soil; this caused fluttering, which persisted for a while since there was no air resistance.*

10.  Sarfati, J., "Exploring the heavens," *Creation* **28**(1):28–32, 2005, creation.com/tigges#moonhoax.

CLAIM: Moon walks were done in studio set. *But the closest we come to such movements is in an airplane falling so fast that it simulates lunar gravity, 1/6 that of Earth.*

## 'The Castenedolo and Calaveras human remains in "old" strata invalidate the geologic column.'

These are not sound examples—the Castenedolo skeletal material shows evidence of being an intrusive burial, i.e. a recent burial into older strata, since all the fossils apart from the human ones had time to be impregnated with salt. The Calaveras skull was probably a hoax planted into a mine by miners.

## 'Dubois renounced Java man as a "missing link" and claimed it was just a giant gibbon.'

Evolutionary anthropology textbooks claimed this, and creationists followed suit. However, this actually misunderstood Dubois, as Stephen Jay Gould has shown. It's true that Dubois claimed that Java man (which he called *Pithecanthropus erectus*) had the proportions of a gibbon. But Dubois had an eccentric view of evolution (universally discounted today) that demanded a precise correlation between brain size and body weight. Dubois' claim about Java man actually *contradicted* the reconstructed evidence of its likely body mass. But it was necessary for Dubois' idiosyncratic proposal that the alleged transitional sequence leading to man fit into a mathematical series. So Dubois' gibbon claim was designed to *reinforce* its 'missing link' status.[11]

## 'The Japanese trawler Zuiyo Maru caught a dead plesiosaur near New Zealand.'

This carcass was almost certainly a rotting basking shark, since their gills and jaws rot rapidly and fall off, leaving the typical small 'neck' with the head. This has been shown by similar specimens washed up on beaches. Also, detailed anatomical and

---

11. See "Who was Java Man?" *Creation* **13**(3):22–23, 1991, creation.com/javaman.

*A decomposing basking shark, rotting to give a "plesiosaur look."*
(Photo by Bev Elliot)

biochemical studies of the Zuiyo-maru carcass show that it could not have been a plesiosaur.[12]

### 'The 2nd Law of Thermodynamics began at the Fall.'

This law says that the entropy ('disorder') of the Universe increases over time, and some have thought that this was the result of the Curse. However, disorder isn't always harmful. An obvious example is digestion, breaking down large complex food molecules into their simple building blocks. Another is friction, which turns ordered mechanical energy into disordered heat—otherwise Adam and Eve would have slipped as they walked with God in Eden! A less obvious example to laymen might be the sun heating the Earth—to a physical chemist, heat transfer from a hot object to a cold one is the classic case of the Second Law in action. Also, breathing is based on another classic Second Law process, gas moving from a high pressure to low pressure. Finally, all beneficial processes in the world, including the development from embryo to adult, increase the overall disorder of the universe, showing that the Second Law is not inherently a curse.

Death and suffering of *nephesh* animals before sin *are* contrary to the biblical framework above, as are suffering (or 'groaning in travail' (Rom. 8:20–22). It is more likely that God withdrew some of His sustaining power (Col. 1:15–17) at the Fall so that the decay

---

12. See Jerlström, P., "Live Plesiosaurs: weighing the evidence," *JoC* **12**(3):339–346, 1998, creation.com/plesiosaurs; Jerlström, P., Elliott, B., "Letting rotting sharks lie," *JoC* **13**(2):83–87, 1999, creation.com/plesiosaurs2; Jerlström, P., de Roos, H., "Parkie: a new 'pseudoplesiosaur' washed up on the Nova Scotia coast," *JoC* **19**(2):109–118, 2005, creation.com/plesiosaurs3.

effect of the Second Law was no longer countered.[13]

## 'If we evolved from apes, why are there still apes today?'

In response to this statement, some evolutionists point out that they don't believe that we descended from apes, but that apes and humans share a common ancestor. However, the

evolutionary paleontologist G.G. Simpson had no time for this 'pussyfooting', as he called it. He said, 'In fact, that earlier ancestor would certainly be called an ape or monkey in popular speech by anyone who saw it. Since the terms ape and monkey are defined by popular usage, man's ancestors were apes or monkeys (or successively both). It is pusillanimous if not dishonest for an informed investigator to say otherwise.'

However, the main point against this statement is that many evolutionists believe that a small group of creatures split off from the main group and became reproductively isolated from the main large population, and that most change happened in the small group which can lead to *allopatric speciation* (a geographically isolated population forming a new species). So there's nothing in evolutionary theory that requires the main group to become extinct.

It's important to note that allopatric speciation is not the sole property of evolutionists—creationists believe that most human variation occurred after small groups became isolated (but not speciated) at Babel, while Adam and Eve probably had mid-brown skin color. The quoted erroneous statement is analogous to saying 'If all people groups came from Adam and Eve, then why are mid-brown people still alive today?'

13. See Sarfati, J., "The second law of thermodynamics, Answers to Critics: Question 3: Did the 2nd Law begin at the Fall?" creation.com/thermo#fall.

So what's the difference between the creationist explanation of people *groups* ('races') and the evolutionist explanation of people *origins*? Answer: the former involves separation of already-existing information and loss of information through mutations; the latter requires the generation of tens of millions of 'letters' of *new* information.

### 'Women have one more rib than men.'

We have long pointed out the fallacy of this statement, which seems to be more popular with dishonest skeptics wanting to caricature creation. The removal of a rib would not affect the *genetic instructions* passed on to the offspring, any more than a man who loses a finger will have sons with nine fingers. Any skeptic who tries to discredit the Bible with this argument must be a closet Lamarckian, i.e. one who believes Lamarck's thoroughly discredited idea of inheritance of acquired characteristics! Note also that Adam wouldn't have had a permanent defect, because the rib is the one bone that can regrow if the surrounding membrane (periosteum) is left intact.[14]

### 'Archaeopteryx is a fraud.'

*Archaeopteryx* was genuine (unlike *Archaeoraptor*, a 'Piltdown bird'[15]), as shown by anatomical studies and close analysis of the fossil slab. It was a true bird, *not* a 'missing link'.

### 'There are no beneficial mutations.'

This is not true, since some changes *do* confer an advantage in some situations. Rather, we should say, 'We have yet to find a mutation that *increases genetic information*, even in those rare instances where the mutation confers an advantage.'

### 'No new species have been produced.'

This is not true—new species have been observed to form. In

14. Wieland, C., "Regenerating ribs," *Creation* 21(4):46–47, 1999, creation.com/rib.

15. Sarfati, J., "Archaeoraptor—phony 'feathered' fossil," 3 February 2000, creation.com/archaeoraptor.

fact, *rapid* speciation is an important part of the creation model. But this speciation is within the 'kind', and involves no new genetic information.

### 'Earth's axis was vertical before the Flood.'

There is no basis for this claim. Seasons are mentioned in Genesis 1:14 *before* the Flood, which strongly suggests an axial tilt from the beginning. Some creationists believe that a change in axial tilt (but not from the vertical) started Noah's Flood. But a lot more evidence is needed and this idea should be regarded as speculative for now. Furthermore, computer modelling suggests that an upright axis would make temperature differences between the poles and equator far *more* extreme than now, while the current tilt of 23.5° is ideal. The Moon has an important function in stabilizing this tilt, and the Moon's large relative size and the fact that its orbital plane is close to the Earth's (unlike most moons in our solar system) are design features.

### 'Paluxy tracks prove that humans and dinosaurs co-existed.'

Some prominent creationist promoters of these tracks have long since withdrawn their support. Some of the allegedly human tracks may be artefacts of erosion of dinosaur tracks obscuring the claw marks. There is a need for properly documented research on the tracks before we would use them to argue the coexistence of humans and dinosaurs.

### Darwin's quote about the absurdity of eye evolution from Origin of Species.

Citing his statement at face value is subtly out of context. Darwin was talking about its seeming absurdity but then said that after all it was quite easy to imagine that the eye could be built step-by-step (in his opinion, with which we obviously disagree).[16]

---

16. Sarfati, J., "Backwardly wired retina 'an optimal structure," 27 May 2010, mueller-v-dawkins.

### 'Earth's division in the days of Peleg (Gen. 10:25) refers to catastrophic splitting of the continents.'

Commentators both before and after Lyell and Darwin (including Calvin, Keil and Delitzsch, and Leupold) are almost unanimous that this passage refers to linguistic division at Babel and subsequent territorial division. We should always interpret Scripture with Scripture, and there's nothing else in Scripture to indicate that this referred to continental division. But only eight verses on (note that chapter and verse divisions were *not* inspired), the Bible states, 'Now the whole earth had one language and one speech' (Gen. 11:1), and as a result of their disobedience, 'the LORD confused the language of all the earth' (Gen. 11:9). This conclusively proves that the 'Earth' that was divided was the same Earth that spoke only one language, i.e. 'Earth' refers *in this context* to the people of the Earth, not Planet Earth.[17]

Another major problem is the scientific consequences of such splitting—another global flood! This gives us the clue as to when the continents did move apart—during Noah's Flood.

### 'The Septuagint records the correct Genesis chronology.'

This is not so. The Septuagint chronologies are demonstrably inflated, and contain the (obvious) error that Methuselah lived 17 years after the Flood. The Masoretic Text (on which almost all English translations are based) preserves the correct chronology.[18]

### 'There are gaps in the genealogies of Genesis 5 and 11 so the Earth may be 10,000 years old or even more.'

This is not so. The language is clear that they are strict chronologies, especially because they give the age of the father

---

17. Sarfati, J., 'In Peleg's days, the earth was divided': what does this mean?, 3 November 2007, creation.com/peleg2.

18. See Williams, P., "Some remarks preliminary to a biblical chronology," *JoC* **12**(1):98–106, 1998, creation.com/chronology.

at the birth of the next name in line. So the Earth is only about 6,000 years old.[19]

### 'Jesus cannot have inherited genetic material from Mary, otherwise He would have inherited original sin.'

This is not stated in Scripture and even *contradicts* important points. The language of the NT indicates physical descent, which must be true for Jesus to have fulfilled the prophecies that He would be a descendant of Abraham, Jacob, Judah and David. Also, the *Protevangelium* of Gen. 3:15, regarded as Messianic by both early Christians and the Jewish Targums, refers to 'the seed of the woman.' This is supported by Gal. 4:4, 'God sent forth His Son, coming (*genomenon*) from a woman.' Most importantly, for Jesus to have died for our sins, Jesus, the 'last Adam' (1 Cor. 15:45), had to share in our humanity (Heb. 2:14), so *must* have been our relative via common descent from the first Adam as Luke 3:38 says. In fact, seven centuries before His Incarnation, the Prophet Isaiah spoke of Him as literally the 'Kinsman-Redeemer', i.e. one who is related by blood to those he redeems (Isaiah 59:20, uses the same Hebrew word *goel* as used to describe Boaz in relation to Naomi). To answer the concern about original sin, the Holy Spirit overshadowed Mary (Luke 1:35), preventing any sin nature being transmitted.[20]

### 'Light was created in transit.'

Some older creationist works, as a solution to the distant starlight problem, proposed that God may have created the light in transit. But CMI long ago pointed out the problems with this idea.

It would entail that we would be seeing light from heavenly bodies that don't really exist; and even light that seems to indicate precise sequences of events predictable by the laws of physics, but which never actually happened. This, in effect, suggests that God is a deceiver.

---

19.  See Sarfati, J., "Biblical chronogenealogies," *JoC* **17**(3):14–18, 2003, creation.com/genealogy, Freeman, T.R., "The Genesis 5 and 11 fluidity question," *JoC* **19**(2):83–90, 2005; creation.com/fluidity.

20.  Sarfati, J., "The virginal conception of Christ," *Apologia* **3**(2):4–11, 1994, reprinted at creation.com/virgin.

For example, when a large star explodes as a supernova, we see a neutrino burst before we see the electromagnetic radiation. This is because most neutrinos pass through solid matter as if it were not there, while light is slowed down. This sequence of events carries information recording an apparently real event. So astronomers are perfectly justified in interpreting this 'message' as a real supernova that exploded according to the laws of physics, with observations as predicted by those same laws.

This is very different from creating Adam as fully grown, looking like a 20-year-old (although incredibly youthful looking), say, although he was really only a few minutes old. Here, there is no deception, because God has *told* us that He created Adam from the dust, not by growing from an infant. But God has also told us that the stars are real, and that they are signs (Genesis 1:14), not just apparitions from light waves.

### 'The phrase "science falsely so called" in 1 Timothy 6:20 (KJV) refers to evolution.'

To develop a scriptural model properly, we must understand what the author *intended* to communicate to his intended audience, which in turn is determined by the grammar and historical context. We must not try to read into Scripture that which appears to support a particular viewpoint. The original Greek word translated 'science' is *gnosis*, and *in this context* refers to the élite esoteric 'knowledge' that was the key to the mystery religions, which later developed into the heresy of *gnosticism*. This was not an *error* by the KJV translators, but an illustration of how many words have *changed their meanings* over time. The word 'science' originally meant 'knowledge', from the Latin *scientia*, from *scio* meaning 'know'. This *original* meaning is just *not* the way it is used today, so modern translations *correctly* render the word as 'knowledge' in this passage.

Of course we believe that evolution *is* anti-knowledge because it clouds the minds of many to the abundant evidence of God's action in Creation and the true knowledge available in His Word, the Bible. But as this chapter points out, it is wrong to use fallacious arguments to support a true viewpoint. On a related matter, it is linguistically fallacious to claim that even now, 'science *really* means knowledge', because meaning is determined by *usage*, not *derivation* (etymology).

### 'Geocentrism (in the classical sense of taking the earth as an absolute reference frame) is taught by Scripture and heliocentrism is anti-scriptural.'

We reject this dogmatic geocentrism, and believes that the biblical passages about sunset etc. should be understood as taking the Earth as a reference frame, but that this is one of many physically valid reference frames; the centre of mass of the solar system is also a valid reference frame.

### 'Ron Wyatt has found Noah's Ark'

This claimed Ark shape is a natural geological formation caused by a mud flow.

### 'Ron Wyatt has found much archaeological proof of the Bible'

There is not the slightest substantiation for Wyatt's claims, just excuses to explain away why the evidence is missing.

### Many of Carl Baugh's creation 'evidences'

Sorry to say, we think that he's well meaning but that he unfortunately uses a lot of material that is not sound scientifically. So we advise against relying on any 'evidence' he provides, unless supported by creationist organisations with reputations for biblical and scientific rigour. Unfortunately, there are talented creationist speakers with reasonably orthodox understandings of Genesis who continue to promote some of the Wyatt and Baugh 'evidences' despite being approached on the matter.

### 'Missing solar neutrinos prove that the sun shines by gravitational collapse, and is proof of a young sun.'

This is about a formerly vexing problem of detecting only one third of the predicted numbers of neutrinos from the sun.

Also, accepted theories of particle physics said that the neutrino had zero rest mass, which would prohibit oscillations from one 'flavour' to another. Therefore, consistent with the data then available, some creationists proposed that the sun was powered one-third by fusion and two-thirds by gravitational collapse. This would have limited the age to far less than 4.5 billion years.

However, a new experiment was able to detect the 'missing' flavours, which seems to provide conclusive evidence for oscillation. This means that neutrinos must have a very tiny rest mass after all—experimental data must take precedence over theory. Therefore creationists should *no longer* invoke the missing neutrino problem to deny that fusion is the primary source of energy for the sun. So it cannot be used as a young-age indicator—nor an old-age indicator for that matter. See Newton, R., Missing neutrinos found! No longer an 'age' indicator, *JoC* **16**(3):123–125, 2002.

### *'Einstein held unswervingly, against enormous peer pressure, to belief in a Creator.'*

However, in the normal meaning of these terms, Einstein believed no such thing.

## What arguments are doubtful, hence inadvisable to use?

### *Canopy theory.*

This is not a direct teaching of Scripture, so there is no place for dogmatism. Also, no suitable model has been developed that holds sufficient water; but some creationists suggest a partial canopy may have been present.

### *'There was no rain before the Flood.'*

This is not a direct teaching of Scripture, so again there should be no dogmatism. Genesis 2:5–6 at face value teaches only that there was no rain at the time Adam was created. But it doesn't rule out rain at any later time before the Flood, as great pre-uniformitarian commentators such as John Calvin pointed out.

A related fallacy is that the rainbow covenant of Genesis 9:12–17 proves that there were no rainbows before the Flood. As Calvin pointed out, God frequently invested existing things with new meanings, e.g. the bread and wine at the Lord's Supper.

## 'Natural selection as tautology.'

Natural selection is in one sense a tautology (i.e., Who are the fittest? Those who survive/leave the most offspring. Who survive/leave the most offspring? The fittest.). But a lot of this is semantic word-play, and depends on how the matter is defined, and for what purpose the definition is raised.

There are many areas of life in which circularity and truth go hand in hand (e.g. What is electric charge? That quality of matter on which an electric field acts. What is an electric field? A region in space that exerts a force on electric charge. But no one would deny that the theory of electricity is valid and can explain how motors work.)—it is only that circularity cannot be used as independent proof of something.

To harp on the issue of tautology can become misleading, if the impression is given that something tautological therefore doesn't happen. Of course the environment can 'select', just as human breeders select. Of course demonstrating this doesn't mean that fish could turn into philosophers by this means—the real issue is the nature of the variation, the information problem. Arguments about tautology distract attention from the real weakness of neo-Darwinism—the source of the new information required. Given an appropriate source of variation (for example, an abundance of created genetic information with the capacity for Mendelian recombination), replicating populations of organisms would be expected to be capable of some adaptation to a given environment, and this has been demonstrated amply in practice.

Natural selection is also a useful explanatory tool in creationist modelling of post-Flood radiation with speciation.

## 'Evolution is just a theory.'

What people usually *mean* when they say this is 'Evolution is not proven fact, so it should not be promoted dogmatically.'

Therefore people should *say* that. The problem with using the word 'theory' in this case is that scientists usually use it to mean a well-substantiated explanation of data. This includes well-known ones such as Einstein's Theory of Relativity and Newton's Theory of Gravity, and lesser-known ones such as the Debye–Hückel Theory of electrolyte solutions and the Deryagin–Landau/Verwey–Overbeek (DLVO) theory of the stability of lyophobic sols, etc. It would be better to say that particles-to-people evolution is an unsubstantiated *hypothesis* or *conjecture*.

All the same, the critic doth protest too much. *Webster's Dictionary* (1996) provides the #2 meaning as 'a proposed explanation whose status is still conjectural, in contrast to well-established propositions that are regarded as reporting matters of actual fact,' and this usage is hardly unknown in the scientific literature. The dictionary further provides '6. contemplation or speculation. 7. guess or conjecture.' So the critic is simply wrong to say that it's a *mistake* to use theory to mean 'speculation', 'conjecture' or 'guess'; and that scientists *never* use theory this way in the literature. So the attack is really cheap point-scoring, but there is still no reason to give critics this diversion.

### 'There is amazing modern scientific insight in the Bible.'

We should interpret the Bible as the author originally intended, and as the intended readership would have understood it. Therefore we should be cautious in reading modern science into passages where the readers would not have seen it. This applies especially to poetic books like Job and Psalms. For example, Job's readers would not have understood Job 38:31 to be teaching anything about gravitational potential energy of Orion and Pleiades. Rather, the original readers would have seen it as a poetic illustration of God's might, i.e. that God, unlike Job, could create the Pleiades in a tightly-knit cluster which is what it looks like; while God created Orion as a well spread out constellation, again something well beyond Job's ability. Similarly, Job 38:14 is *not* advanced scientific insight into the earth's rotation, because the earth is *not* being compared to the turning seal but to the *clay* turning *from one shape into another* under the seal.

## 'Laminin: an amazing illustration of how Jesus is holding each of us together.'

That one protein out of 100,000 is shaped like a cross in formalized diagrams (probably more like a sword with the side arms not at right angles) is not that surprising, just 'by chance'. In any case, Jesus is sustaining our creation *from God the Father's right hand*; He is *no longer on the cross*, so the theology is dubious too.

## 'The speed of light has decreased over time' (c decay).

Although most of the evolutionary counter-arguments have been proven to be fallacious, there are still a number of problems, many of which were raised by creationists, which we believe have not been satisfactorily answered. CMI currently believes that both Dr Russell Humphreys' and Dr John Hartnett's cosmologies (both involving relativistic time dilation) provide viable solutions for the distant starlight problem. It's a healthy situation to have multiple working hypotheses at the moment because there are so many unknowns in astronomy and cosmology. However, neither we, Dr Humphreys nor Dr Hartnett claim that either of these models are infallible.

## 'There are no transitional forms.'

Since there are *candidates*, even though they are highly dubious, it's better to avoid possible comebacks by saying instead: 'While Darwin predicted that the fossil record would show numerous transitional fossils, even 140 years later, all we have are a handful of disputable examples.'

## 'Gold chains have been found in coal.'

Several artefacts, including gold objects, have been documented as having been found within coal, but in each case the coal is no longer associated with the artefact. The evidence is therefore strictly anecdotal (e.g. 'This object was left behind in the fireplace after a lump of coal was burned'). This does not have the same evidential value as having a specimen with the coal and the artefact still associated.

### 'Plate tectonics is fallacious.'

CMI believes that Dr John Baumgardner's work on Catastrophic Plate Tectonics provides a good explanation of continental shifts and the Flood. However, we recognise that some reputable creationist scientists disagree with plate tectonics.

### 'Creationists believe in microevolution but not macroevolution.'

These terms, which focus on 'small' v. 'large' changes, distract from the key issue of *information*. That is, particles-to-people evolution requires changes that *increase* genetic information (e.g., specifications for manufacturing nerves, muscle, bone, etc.), but all we observe is *sorting* and, overwhelmingly, *loss* of information. We are hardpressed to find examples of even 'micro' increases in information, although such changes should be frequent if evolution were true. Conversely, we do observe quite 'macro' changes that involve *no* new information, e.g. when a control gene is switched on or off. Interestingly, even high profile evolutionists (e.g. Mayr, Ayala) disagree with the idea that the observed small changes in living things are sufficient to account for the grand scheme of microbes-to-mankind evolution.

### 'The Gospel is in the stars.'

This is an interesting idea, but quite speculative, and many biblical creationists doubt that it is taught in Scripture, so we do not recommend using it.

# Index

# RECOMMENDED RESOURCES

## REFUTING EVOLUTION

The precursor to this sequel, *Refuting Evolution* is a hard-hitting critique of the most common arguments for evolution, to challenge educators, students, and parents. It is a powerful yet concise summary of the arguments against evolution and for creation. It will stimulate much discussion and help students and teachers think more critically about origins.

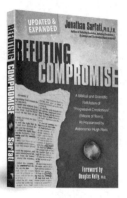

## REFUTING COMPROMISE

With his usual brilliant clarity, Jonathan Sarfati, author of the best-selling *Refuting Evolution* (Vols. 1 and 2) has produced a comprehensive and resounding refutation of the position of 'progressive creationist' Hugh Ross, whose views are causing massive confusion about science and the Bible. The most powerful theological and scientific defence of a straightforward view of Genesis creation ever written.

## THE CREATION ANSWERS BOOK

*The Creation Answers Book* provides biblical answers to over 60 important questions that everyone wants to know about creation/evolution and the Bible, like "What about dinosaurs, carbon-14 dating, and who was Cain's wife?" Not only will it answer your questions, but it will equip you to effectively respond to the questions of others. This important work is a must have for anyone's library.

*For more information visit*

# CREATION.com

# CREATION.com

For more information on creation/evolution and Bible-science issues

**AUSTRALIA**
*Creation Ministries International (Australia)*
PO Box 4545
Eight Mile Plains, QLD 4113

**Phone:** (07) 3340 9888
**Fax:** (07) 3340 9889
ABN 31 010 120 304

**CANADA**
*Creation Ministries International (Canada)*
300 Mill St, Unit 7
Kitchener, ON N2M 5G8

**Phone:** (519) 746–7616
**Orders & donations:** 1-888-251-5360
**Fax:** (519) 746–7617

**NEW ZEALAND**
*Creation Ministries International (NZ)*
PO Box 39005
Howick, Auckland 2145

**Phone/Fax:** (09) 537 4818
A Registered Charitable Trust

**SINGAPORE**
*Creation Ministries International (Singapore)*
Clementi Central Post Office
PO Box 195
Singapore 911207

**Phone:** 9698 4292

**SOUTH AFRICA**
*Creation Ministries International (SA)*
PO Box 3349
Durbanville 7551

**Phone:** (021) 979 0107
**Fax:** (086) 519 0555

**UK & Europe**
*Creation Ministries International
(UK/Europe)*
15 Station St,
Whetstone, Leicestershire, LE8 6JS

**Phone:** 0116-2848-999

**USA**
*Creation Ministries International (USA)*
PO Box 350,
Powder Springs, GA 30127

**Phone:** (800) 616-1264
**Fax:** (770) 439-9784

**OTHER COUNTRIES**
*Creation Ministries International*
PO Box 4545
Eight Mile Plains,
QLD 4113, Australia

**Phone:** +617 3340 9888
**Fax:** +617 3340 9889